EYEWITNESS VISUAL DICTIONARIES

THE VISUAL DICTIONARY *of*
DINOSAURS

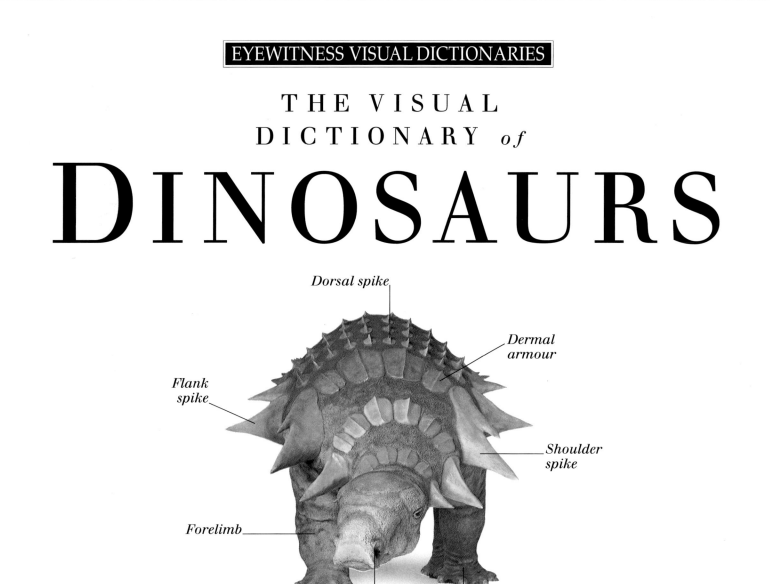

Dorsal spike

Dermal armour

Flank spike

Shoulder spike

Forelimb

Naris

Forefoot

EXTERNAL FEATURES OF EDMONTONIA

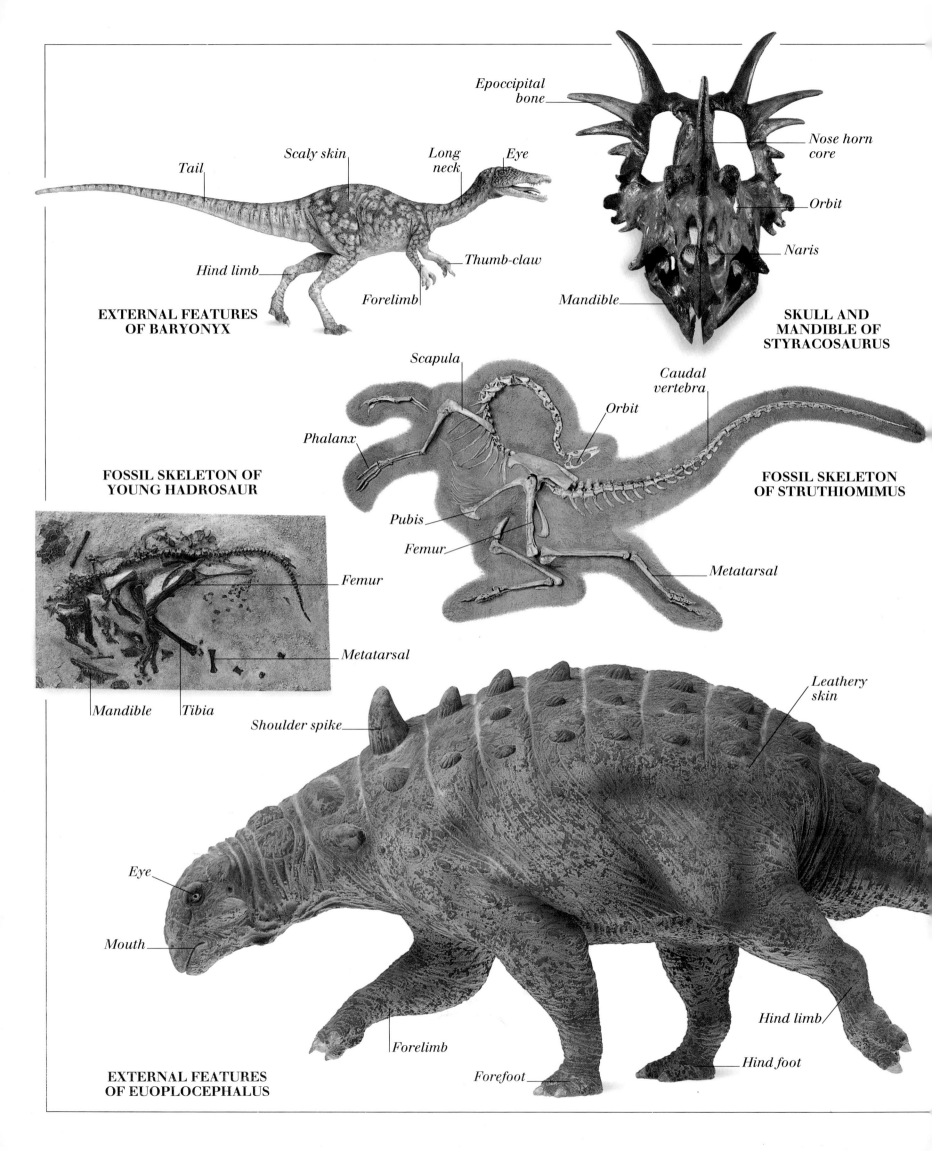

Tail

Scaly skin

Long neck

Eye

Epoccipital bone

Nose horn core

Hind limb

Thumb-claw

Orbit

Forelimb

Naris

EXTERNAL FEATURES OF BARYONYX

Mandible

SKULL AND MANDIBLE OF STYRACOSAURUS

Scapula

Caudal vertebra

Phalanx

Orbit

FOSSIL SKELETON OF YOUNG HADROSAUR

Pubis

Femur

FOSSIL SKELETON OF STRUTHIOMIMUS

Femur

Metatarsal

Mandible

Tibia

Metatarsal

Leathery skin

Shoulder spike

Eye

Mouth

Hind limb

Forelimb

EXTERNAL FEATURES OF EUOPLOCEPHALUS

Forefoot

Hind foot

EYEWITNESS VISUAL DICTIONARIES

THE VISUAL
DICTIONARY *of*
DINOSAURS

Emerged
hatchling

Eggshell

Nest
material

MODEL OF ORODROMEUS NEST

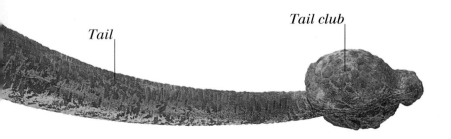

Tail

Tail club

DORLING KINDERSLEY

LONDON • NEW YORK • STUTTGART

A DORLING KINDERSLEY BOOK

Project Art Editor Clare Shedden
Designer Ellen Woodward

Project Editors Fiona Courtenay-Thompson, Mary Lindsay
Consultant Editors David Lambert, Dr Ralph E. Molnar

Managing Art Editor Stephen Knowlden
Senior Editor Martyn Page
Managing Editor Ruth Midgley

Photography Andy Crawford
Illustrations John Temperton, Graham Rosewarne
Model Makers John Holmes, Roby Braun, Graham High and Jeremy Hunt (Centaur Studios)

Production Hilary Stephens

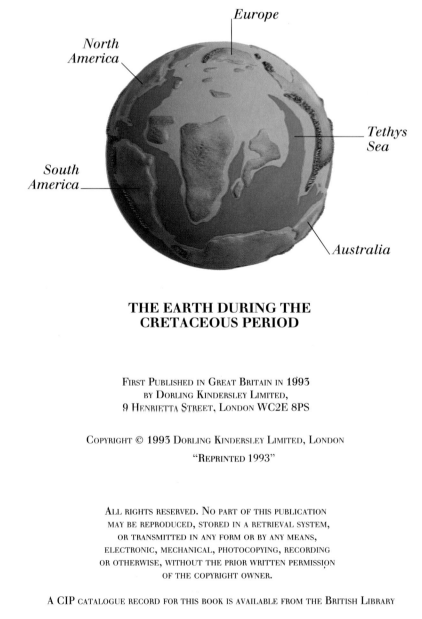

North
America

Europe

Tethys
Sea

South
America

Australia

**THE EARTH DURING THE
CRETACEOUS PERIOD**

First Published in Great Britain in 1993
by Dorling Kindersley Limited,
9 Henrietta Street, London WC2E 8PS

Copyright © 1993 Dorling Kindersley Limited, London

"Reprinted 1993"

A CIP catalogue record for this book is available from the British Library

ISBN 0-7513-1012-3

Reproduced by Colourscan, Singapore
Printed and bound by Arnoldo Mondadori, Verona, Italy

Contents

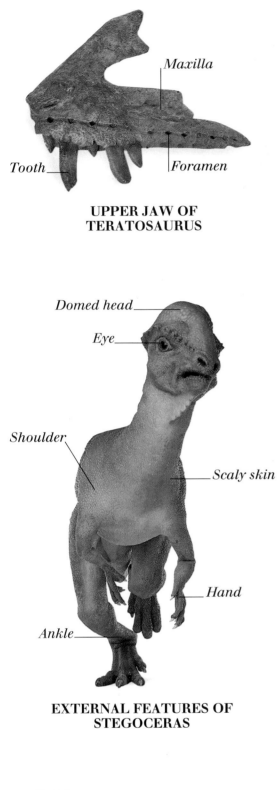

Maxilla

Tooth

Foramen

UPPER JAW OF TERATOSAURUS

Domed head

Eye

Shoulder

Scaly skin

Hand

Ankle

EXTERNAL FEATURES OF STEGOCERAS

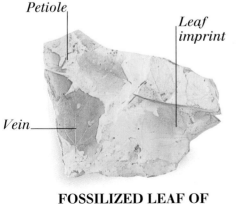

Petiole

Leaf imprint

Vein

FOSSILIZED LEAF OF CRETACEOUS TREE

Cranium

Orbit

Naris

Beak

Mandible

SKULL AND MANDIBLE OF EUOPLOCEPHALUS

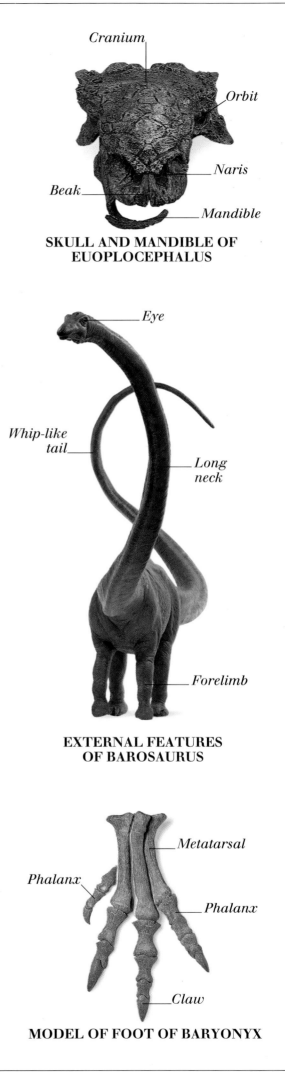

Eye

Whip-like tail

Long neck

Forelimb

EXTERNAL FEATURES OF BAROSAURUS

Metatarsal

Phalanx

Phalanx

Claw

MODEL OF FOOT OF BARYONYX

The dinosaurs

DINOSAURS WERE A LARGE GROUP OF REPTILES that were the dominant land vertebrates (animals with backbones) on Earth from the first part of the Late Triassic (231 million years ago) to the end of the Cretaceous period (65 million years ago). Dinosaurs were diverse, ranging from huge herbivores (plant-eaters) such as *Barosaurus*, which was 27.4 m (90 ft) long, to small carnivores (flesh-eaters) such as *Compsognathus*, which was less than 1.4 m (4 ft 8 in) long. Two features that most dinosaurs had in common were raised metatarsals and an erect stance. Their erect stance enabled dinosaurs to keep their bodies well above the ground, unlike the sprawling and semi-sprawling stances of other reptiles. Dinosaurs can be categorized into two main groups according to the structure of their pelvis (hip bones): ornithischian (bird-hipped) and saurischian (lizard-hipped) dinosaurs. Ornithischians had a relatively long, shallow ilium and a backward-slanting pubis. Most saurischians had a shorter, deeper ilium and a forward-slanting pubis. A third, small group of dinosaurs, the herrerasaurs, had pelvic bones similar to those of saurischians.

COMPARISON OF ANIMAL STANCES

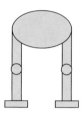

ERECT STANCE
The thighs and upper arms project straight down from the body so that the knees and elbows are straight.

BAROSAURUS
A saurischian dinosaur

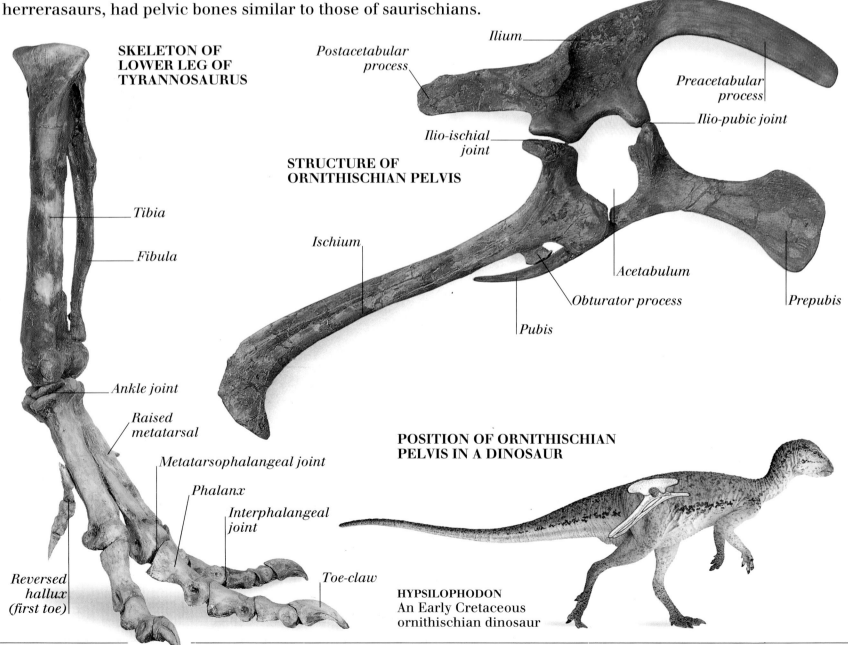

SKELETON OF LOWER LEG OF TYRANNOSAURUS

Tibia

Fibula

Ankle joint

Raised metatarsal

Metatarsophalangeal joint

Phalanx

Interphalangeal joint

Reversed hallux (first toe)

Toe-claw

Postacetabular process

Ilium

Preacetabular process

Ilio-pubic joint

Ilio-ischial joint

STRUCTURE OF ORNITHISCHIAN PELVIS

Ischium

Acetabulum

Obturator process

Prepubis

Pubis

POSITION OF ORNITHISCHIAN PELVIS IN A DINOSAUR

HYPSILOPHODON
An Early Cretaceous ornithischian dinosaur

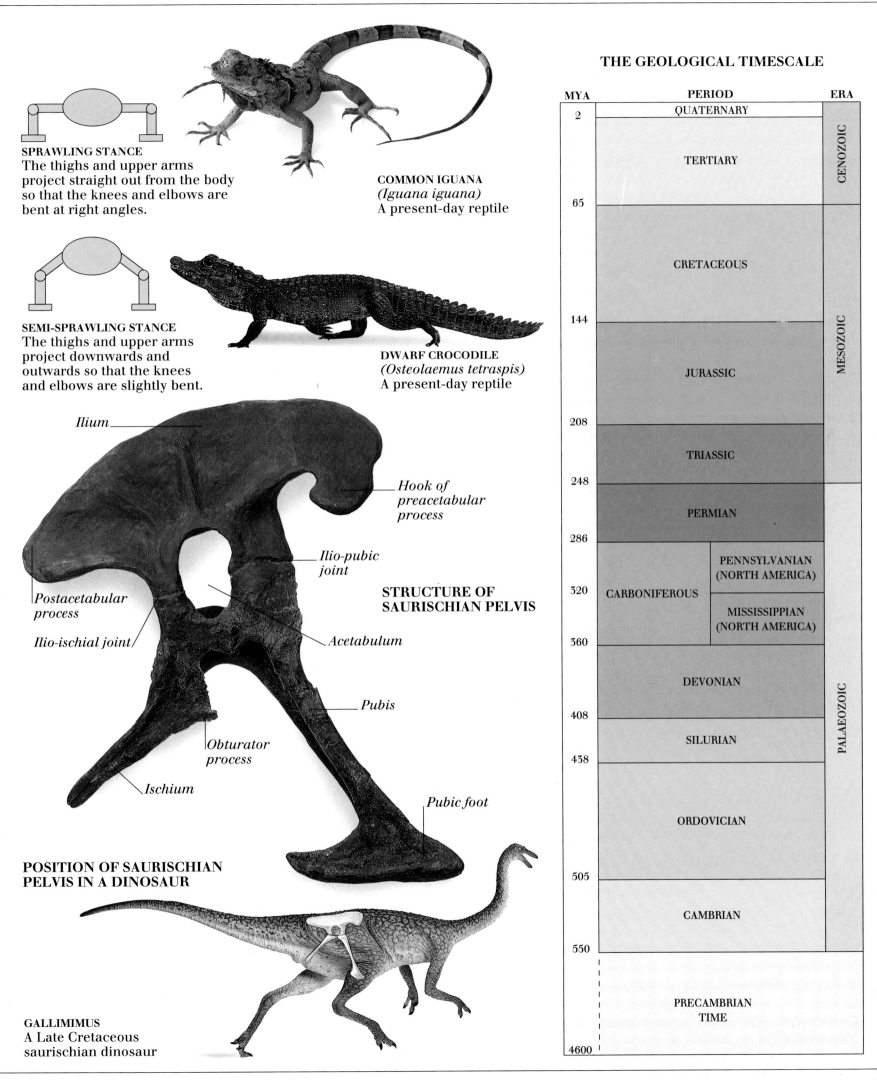

SPRAWLING STANCE
The thighs and upper arms
project straight out from the body
so that the knees and elbows are
bent at right angles.

COMMON IGUANA
(*Iguana iguana*)
A present-day reptile

SEMI-SPRAWLING STANCE
The thighs and upper arms
project downwards and
outwards so that the knees
and elbows are slightly bent.

DWARF CROCODILE
(*Osteolaemus tetraspis*)
A present-day reptile

Ilium

*Hook of
preacetabular
process*

*Ilio-pubic
joint*

**STRUCTURE OF
SAURISCHIAN PELVIS**

*Postacetabular
process*

Ilio-ischial joint

Acetabulum

Pubis

*Obturator
process*

Ischium

Pubic foot

**POSITION OF SAURISCHIAN
PELVIS IN A DINOSAUR**

GALLIMIMUS
A Late Cretaceous
saurischian dinosaur

THE GEOLOGICAL TIMESCALE

MYA	PERIOD		ERA
2	QUATERNARY		CENOZOIC
	TERTIARY		
65	CRETACEOUS		
144	JURASSIC		MESOZOIC
208	TRIASSIC		
248	PERMIAN		
286	CARBONIFEROUS	PENNSYLVANIAN (NORTH AMERICA)	
320		MISSISSIPPIAN (NORTH AMERICA)	
360	DEVONIAN		PALAEOZOIC
408	SILURIAN		
438	ORDOVICIAN		
505	CAMBRIAN		
550			
	PRECAMBRIAN TIME		
4600			

7

Triassic period

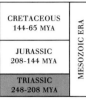
THE TRIASSIC PERIOD (248–208 million years ago) marked the beginning of what is known as the Age of the Dinosaurs (the Mesozoic era). During this period the present-day continents were massed together, forming one huge continent known as Pangaea. This landmass experienced extremes of climate, with lush green areas around the coast or by lakes and rivers, and arid deserts in the interior. The only forms of plant life were non-flowering plants, such as conifers, ferns, cycads, and ginkgos; flowering plants had not yet evolved. The principal forms of animal life included primitive amphibians, rhynchosaurs ("beaked lizards"), and primitive crocodilians. Dinosaurs first appeared about 230 million years ago, at the beginning of the Late Triassic. The earliest known dinosaurs were the carnivorous (flesh-eating) herrerasaurids and staurikosaurids, such as *Herrerasaurus* and *Staurikosaurus*. Early herbivorous (plant-eating) dinosaurs first appeared in the Late Triassic and included *Plateosaurus* and *Technosaurus*. By the end of the Triassic, dinosaurs dominated Pangaea, possibly contributing to the extinction of many other reptiles.

TRIASSIC POSITIONS OF PRESENT-DAY LANDMASSES

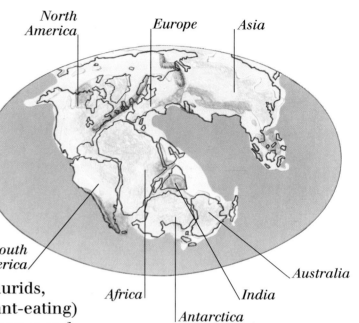

North America

Europe

Asia

South America

Africa

Antarctica

India

Australia

EXAMPLES OF TRIASSIC PLANT GROUPS

A PRESENT-DAY CYCAD
(*Cycas revoluta*)

A PRESENT-DAY GINKGO
(*Ginkgo biloba*)

A PRESENT-DAY CONIFER
(*Araucaria araucana*)

AN EXTINCT FERN
(*Pachypteris sp.*)

AN EXTINCT CYCAD
(*Cycas sp.*)

EXAMPLES OF TRIASSIC DINOSAURS

STAURIKOSAURUS
A staurikosaurid
Length: 2 m (6 ft 6 in)

COELOPHYSIS
A coelophysid
Length: 3 m (10 ft)

TECHNOSAURUS
A primitive ornithischian
Length: 1 m (3 ft 3 in)

PLATEOSAURUS
A plateosaurid
Length: 7.9 m (26 ft)

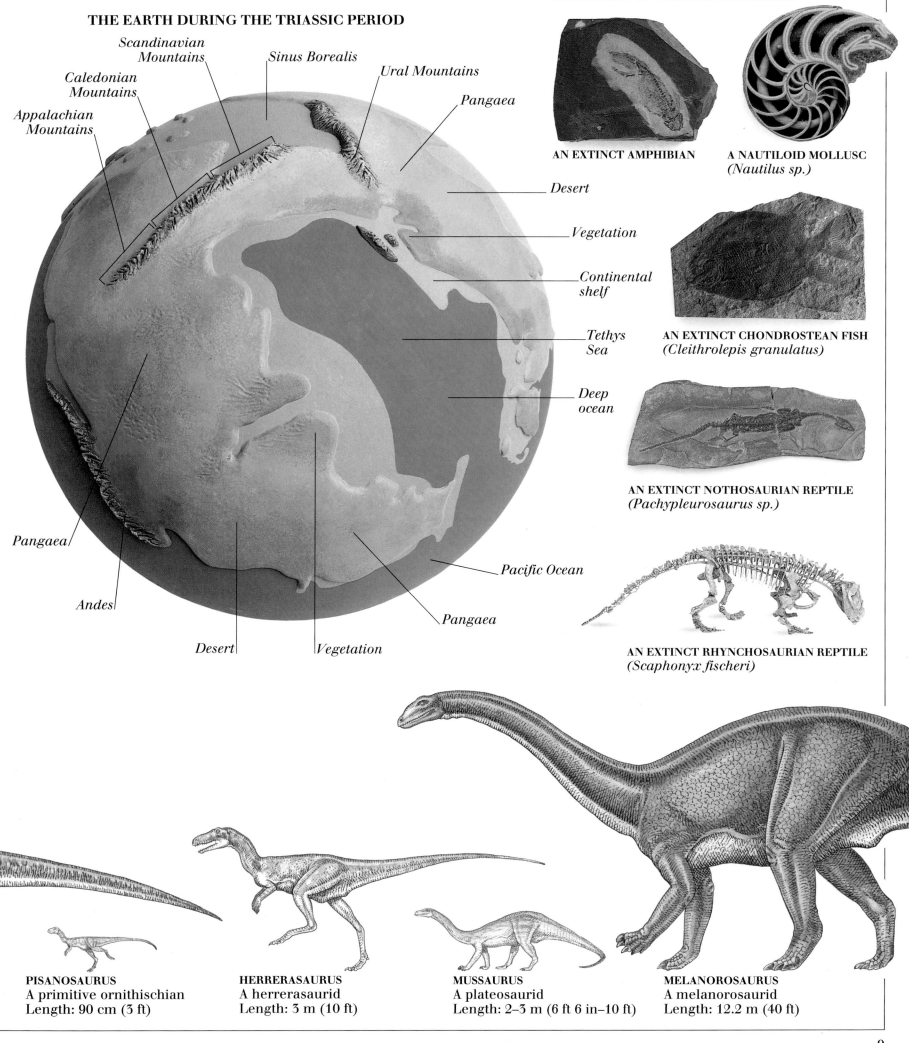

THE EARTH DURING THE TRIASSIC PERIOD

Scandinavian Mountains

Caledonian Mountains

Appalachian Mountains

Sinus Borealis

Ural Mountains

Pangaea

Desert

Vegetation

Continental shelf

Tethys Sea

Deep ocean

Pacific Ocean

Pangaea

Pangaea

Andes

Desert

Vegetation

EXAMPLES OF TRIASSIC ANIMALS

AN EXTINCT AMPHIBIAN

A NAUTILOID MOLLUSC
(*Nautilus sp.*)

AN EXTINCT CHONDROSTEAN FISH
(*Cleithrolepis granulatus*)

AN EXTINCT NOTHOSAURIAN REPTILE
(*Pachypleurosaurus sp.*)

AN EXTINCT RHYNCHOSAURIAN REPTILE
(*Scaphonyx fischeri*)

PISANOSAURUS
A primitive ornithischian
Length: 90 cm (3 ft)

HERRERASAURUS
A herrerasaurid
Length: 3 m (10 ft)

MUSSAURUS
A plateosaurid
Length: 2–3 m (6 ft 6 in–10 ft)

MELANOROSAURUS
A melanorosaurid
Length: 12.2 m (40 ft)

Jurassic period

CRETACEOUS 144-65 MYA	
JURASSIC 208-144 MYA	MESOZOIC ERA
TRIASSIC 248-208 MYA	

THE JURASSIC PERIOD, the middle part of the Mesozoic era, lasted from 208 to 144 million years ago. During the Jurassic, the landmass of Pangaea broke up into the continents of Gondwanaland and Laurasia, and sea levels rose, flooding areas of lower land. The Jurassic climate was warm and moist. Plants such as ginkgos, horsetails, and conifers thrived, and giant redwood trees appeared, as did the first flowering plants. The abundance of plant food led to the proliferation of herbivorous (plant-eating) dinosaurs, such as the large sauropods (e.g., *Diplodocus*) and stegosaurs (e.g., *Stegosaurus*). Carnivorous (flesh-eating) dinosaurs, such as *Compsognathus* and *Allosaurus*, also flourished by hunting the many animals, including other dinosaurs, that existed. Other Jurassic animals included shrew-like mammals, and pterosaurs (flying reptiles), as well as plesiosaurs and ichthyosaurs (both marine reptiles).

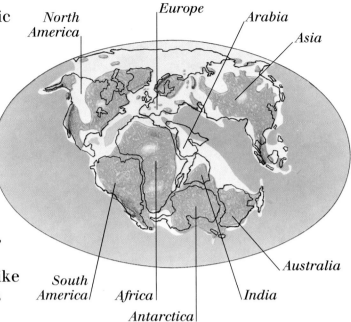

North America
Europe
Arabia
Asia
South America
Africa
Antarctica
India
Australia

EXAMPLES OF JURASSIC PLANT GROUPS

A PRESENT-DAY FERN
(Dicksonia antarctica)

A PRESENT-DAY HORSETAIL
(Equisetum arvense)

A PRESENT-DAY CONIFER
(Taxus baccata)

AN EXTINCT CONIFER

AN EXTINCT REDWOOD
(Sequoiadendron sp.)

EXAMPLES OF JURASSIC DINOSAURS

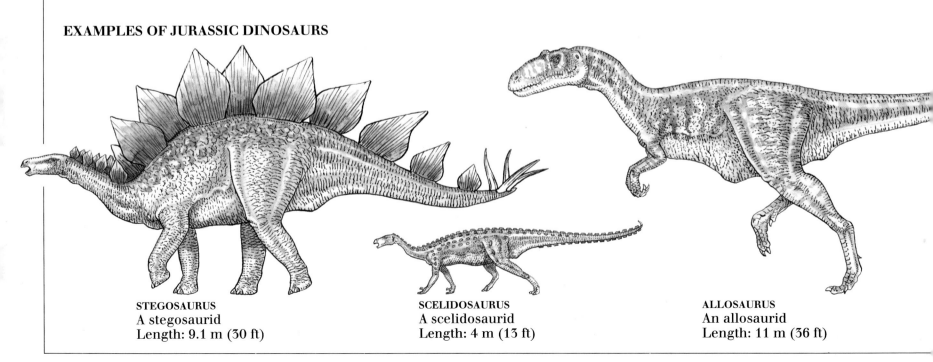

STEGOSAURUS
A stegosaurid
Length: 9.1 m (30 ft)

SCELIDOSAURUS
A scelidosaurid
Length: 4 m (13 ft)

ALLOSAURUS
An allosaurid
Length: 11 m (36 ft)

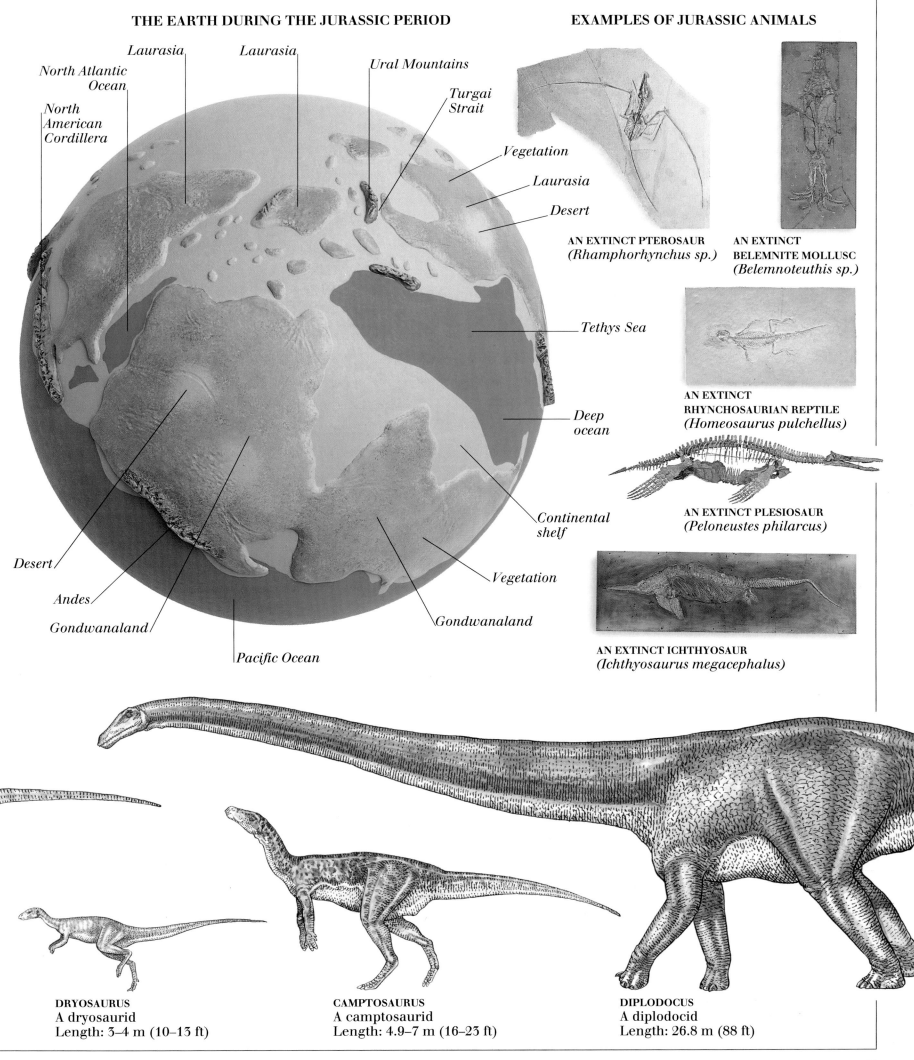

THE EARTH DURING THE JURASSIC PERIOD

North Atlantic Ocean

North American Cordillera

Laurasia

Laurasia

Ural Mountains

Turgai Strait

Vegetation

Laurasia

Desert

Tethys Sea

Deep ocean

Continental shelf

Vegetation

Gondwanaland

Desert

Andes

Gondwanaland

Pacific Ocean

EXAMPLES OF JURASSIC ANIMALS

AN EXTINCT PTEROSAUR
(*Rhamphorhynchus sp.*)

AN EXTINCT BELEMNITE MOLLUSC
(*Belemnoteuthis sp.*)

AN EXTINCT RHYNCHOSAURIAN REPTILE
(*Homeosaurus pulchellus*)

AN EXTINCT PLESIOSAUR
(*Peloneustes philarcus*)

AN EXTINCT ICHTHYOSAUR
(*Ichthyosaurus megacephalus*)

DRYOSAURUS
A dryosaurid
Length: 3–4 m (10–13 ft)

CAMPTOSAURUS
A camptosaurid
Length: 4.9–7 m (16–23 ft)

DIPLODOCUS
A diplodocid
Length: 26.8 m (88 ft)

Cretaceous period

CRETACEOUS 144-65 MYA	
JURASSIC 208-144 MYA	MESOZOIC ERA
TRIASSIC 248-208 MYA	

THE MESOZOIC ERA ENDED WITH the Cretaceous period, which lasted from 144 to 65 million years ago. During this period, Gondwanaland and Laurasia were breaking up into smaller landmasses that more closely resembled those of the modern continents. The climate remained mild and moist but the seasons became more marked. Flowering plants, including deciduous trees, replaced many cycads, seed ferns, and conifers. Animal species became more varied, with the evolution of new mammals, insects, fish, crustaceans, and turtles. Dinosaurs evolved into a wide variety of species during the Cretaceous; more than half of all known dinosaurs – including *Iguanodon*, *Deinonychus*, *Tyrannosaurus*, and *Hypsilophodon* – lived during this period. At the end of the Cretaceous, however, dinosaurs became extinct. The reason for this mass extinction is unknown but it is thought to have been caused by climatic changes due to either a catastrophic meteor impact with the Earth or extensive volcanic eruptions.

North America · *Europe* · *Asia* · *Arabia* · *South America* · *Africa* · *Antarctica* · *India* · *Australia*

EXAMPLES OF CRETACEOUS PLANT GROUPS

A PRESENT-DAY CONIFER
(Pinus muricata)

A PRESENT-DAY DECIDUOUS TREE
(Magnolia sp.)

AN EXTINCT FERN
(Sphenopteris latiloba)

AN EXTINCT GINKGO
(Ginkgo pluripartita)

AN EXTINCT DECIDUOUS TREE
(Cercidyphyllum sp.)

EXAMPLES OF CRETACEOUS DINOSAURS

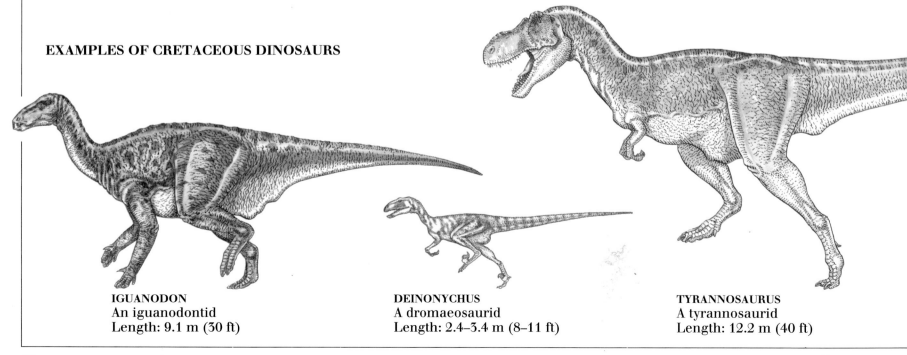

IGUANODON
An iguanodontid
Length: 9.1 m (30 ft)

DEINONYCHUS
A dromaeosaurid
Length: 2.4–3.4 m (8–11 ft)

TYRANNOSAURUS
A tyrannosaurid
Length: 12.2 m (40 ft)

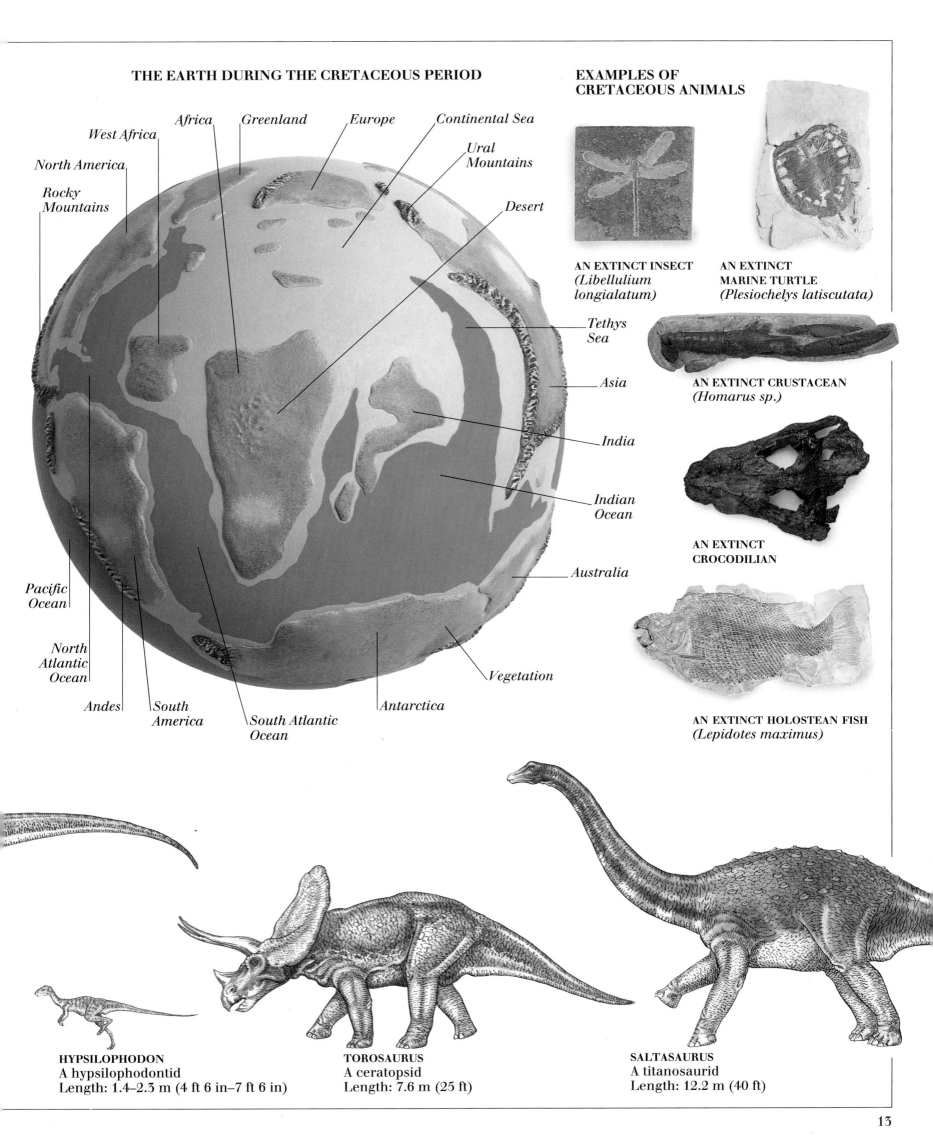

THE EARTH DURING THE CRETACEOUS PERIOD

North America
West Africa
Africa
Greenland
Europe
Continental Sea
Ural Mountains
Rocky Mountains
Desert
Tethys Sea
Asia
India
Indian Ocean
Australia
Pacific Ocean
North Atlantic Ocean
Andes
South America
South Atlantic Ocean
Antarctica
Vegetation

EXAMPLES OF CRETACEOUS ANIMALS

AN EXTINCT INSECT
(*Libellulium longialatum*)

AN EXTINCT MARINE TURTLE
(*Plesiochelys latiscutata*)

AN EXTINCT CRUSTACEAN
(*Homarus sp.*)

AN EXTINCT CROCODILIAN

AN EXTINCT HOLOSTEAN FISH
(*Lepidotes maximus*)

HYPSILOPHODON
A hypsilophodontid
Length: 1.4–2.3 m (4 ft 6 in–7 ft 6 in)

TOROSAURUS
A ceratopsid
Length: 7.6 m (25 ft)

SALTASAURUS
A titanosaurid
Length: 12.2 m (40 ft)

13

Small theropods

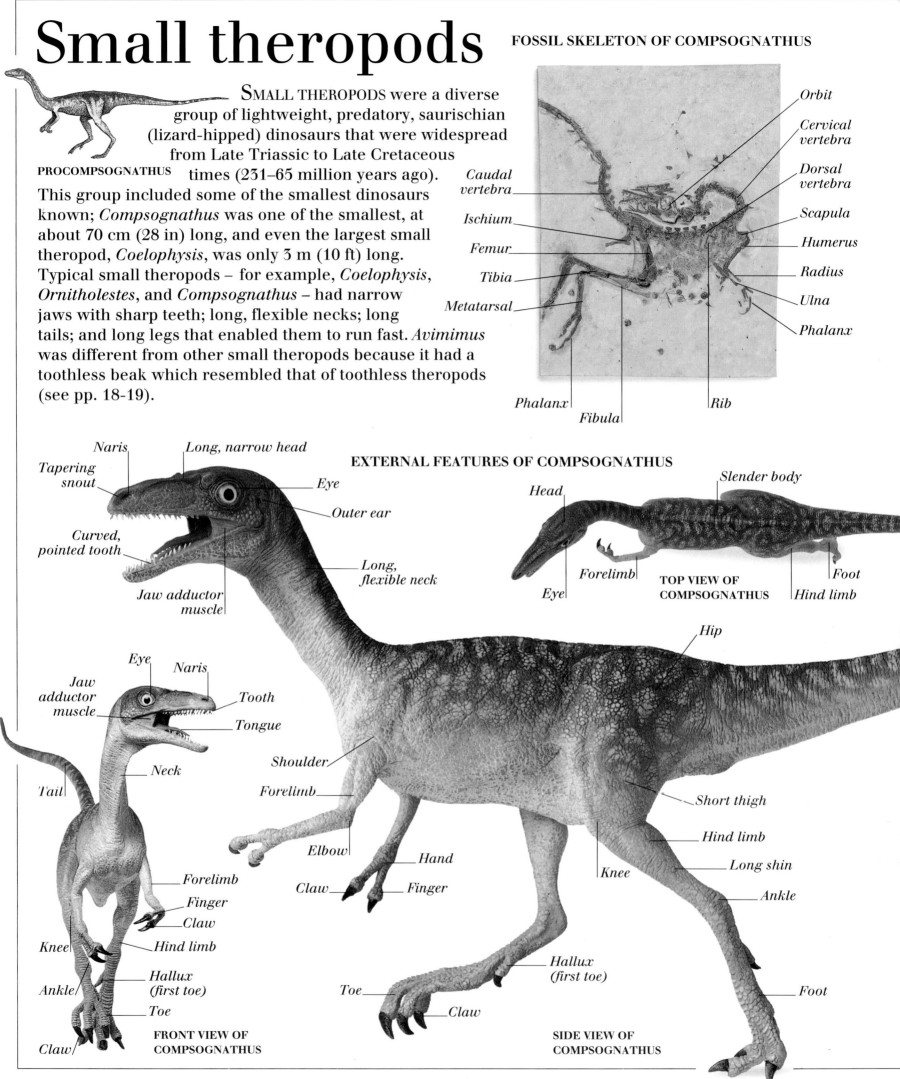

SMALL THEROPODS were a diverse group of lightweight, predatory, saurischian (lizard-hipped) dinosaurs that were widespread from Late Triassic to Late Cretaceous times (231–65 million years ago). This group included some of the smallest dinosaurs known; *Compsognathus* was one of the smallest, at about 70 cm (28 in) long, and even the largest small theropod, *Coelophysis*, was only 3 m (10 ft) long. Typical small theropods – for example, *Coelophysis*, *Ornitholestes*, and *Compsognathus* – had narrow jaws with sharp teeth; long, flexible necks; long tails; and long legs that enabled them to run fast. *Avimimus* was different from other small theropods because it had a toothless beak which resembled that of toothless theropods (see pp. 18-19).

PROCOMPSOGNATHUS

Orbit

Cervical vertebra

Dorsal vertebra

Scapula

Humerus

Radius

Ulna

Phalanx

Caudal vertebra

Ischium

Femur

Tibia

Metatarsal

Phalanx

Fibula

Rib

EXTERNAL FEATURES OF COMPSOGNATHUS

Naris

Long, narrow head

Tapering snout

Eye

Outer ear

Curved, pointed tooth

Jaw adductor muscle

Long, flexible neck

Head

Slender body

Forelimb

Eye

Foot

TOP VIEW OF COMPSOGNATHUS

Hind limb

Hip

Eye

Naris

Jaw adductor muscle

Tooth

Tongue

Neck

Tail

Shoulder

Forelimb

Short thigh

Hind limb

Long shin

Knee

Ankle

Elbow

Hand

Claw

Finger

Forelimb

Finger

Claw

Hind limb

Knee

Ankle

Hallux (first toe)

Toe

Claw

Hallux (first toe)

Toe

Claw

Foot

FRONT VIEW OF COMPSOGNATHUS

SIDE VIEW OF COMPSOGNATHUS

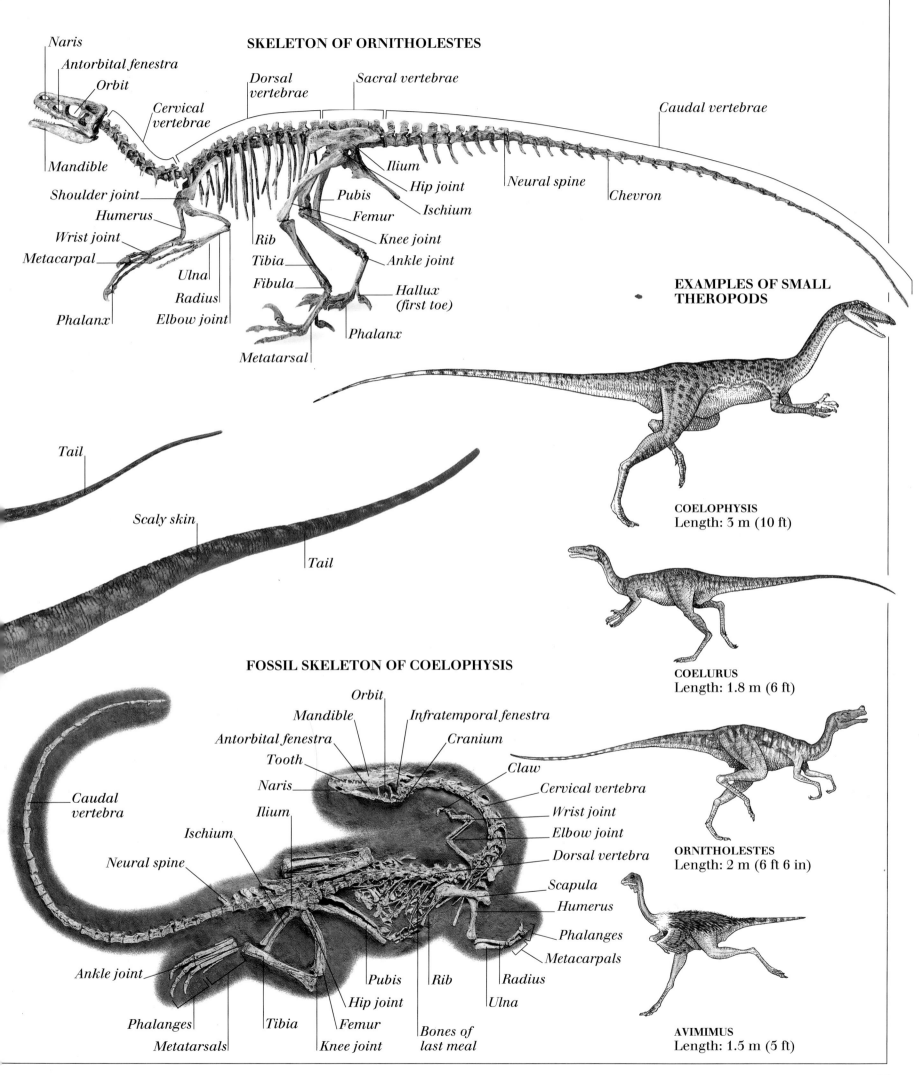

SKELETON OF ORNITHOLESTES

Naris

Antorbital fenestra

Orbit

Dorsal vertebrae

Sacral vertebrae

Caudal vertebrae

Cervical vertebrae

Mandible

Ilium

Hip joint

Neural spine

Chevron

Shoulder joint

Pubis

Ischium

Humerus

Femur

Wrist joint

Knee joint

Metacarpal

Rib

Ankle joint

Ulna

Tibia

Radius

Fibula

Hallux (first toe)

Phalanx

Elbow joint

Phalanx

Metatarsal

EXAMPLES OF SMALL THEROPODS

Tail

Scaly skin

Tail

COELOPHYSIS
Length: 3 m (10 ft)

COELURUS
Length: 1.8 m (6 ft)

FOSSIL SKELETON OF COELOPHYSIS

Orbit

Mandible

Infratemporal fenestra

Antorbital fenestra

Cranium

Tooth

Claw

Caudal vertebra

Naris

Cervical vertebra

Ilium

Wrist joint

Ischium

Elbow joint

Neural spine

Dorsal vertebra

Scapula

Humerus

Phalanges

Metacarpals

Ankle joint

Radius

Ulna

Phalanges

Tibia

Pubis

Rib

Metatarsals

Hip joint

Femur

Knee joint

Bones of last meal

ORNITHOLESTES
Length: 2 m (6 ft 6 in)

AVIMIMUS
Length: 1.5 m (5 ft)

Deinonychosaurs

DEINONYCHOSAURS WERE A GROUP of ferocious, predatory, saurischian (lizard-hipped) dinosaurs that lived in northern continents during the Cretaceous period (144–65 million years ago). The characteristic feature of these dinosaurs is a large, sickle-shaped claw on their second toe (deinonychosaur means "terrible claw lizard"). This claw flicked forwards to slash prey during an attack. Deinonychosaurs were relatively small – ranging from about 1.8 m (6 ft) to 4 m (13 ft) in length – and agile, running on their powerful hind legs and using their long, stiff tail to keep balance and also to help change direction quickly by acting as a rudder. It was thought that deinonychosaurs comprised two main subgroups – dromaeosaurids, such as *Deinonychus* and *Dromaeosaurus*, and troodontids, such as *Troodon* – but recent evidence suggests that dromaeosaurids and troodontids are not as closely related as previously believed. Dromaeosaurids had eyes at the side of the head, giving them a wide angle of vision. Their "terrible claws" were large and, by hunting in packs, dromaeosaurids could bring down prey much larger than themselves. In contrast, troodontids had smaller "terrible claws" and large, forward-facing eyes, which may have given them three-dimensional vision. Troodontids had larger brains, relative to their body size, than any other known dinosaur.

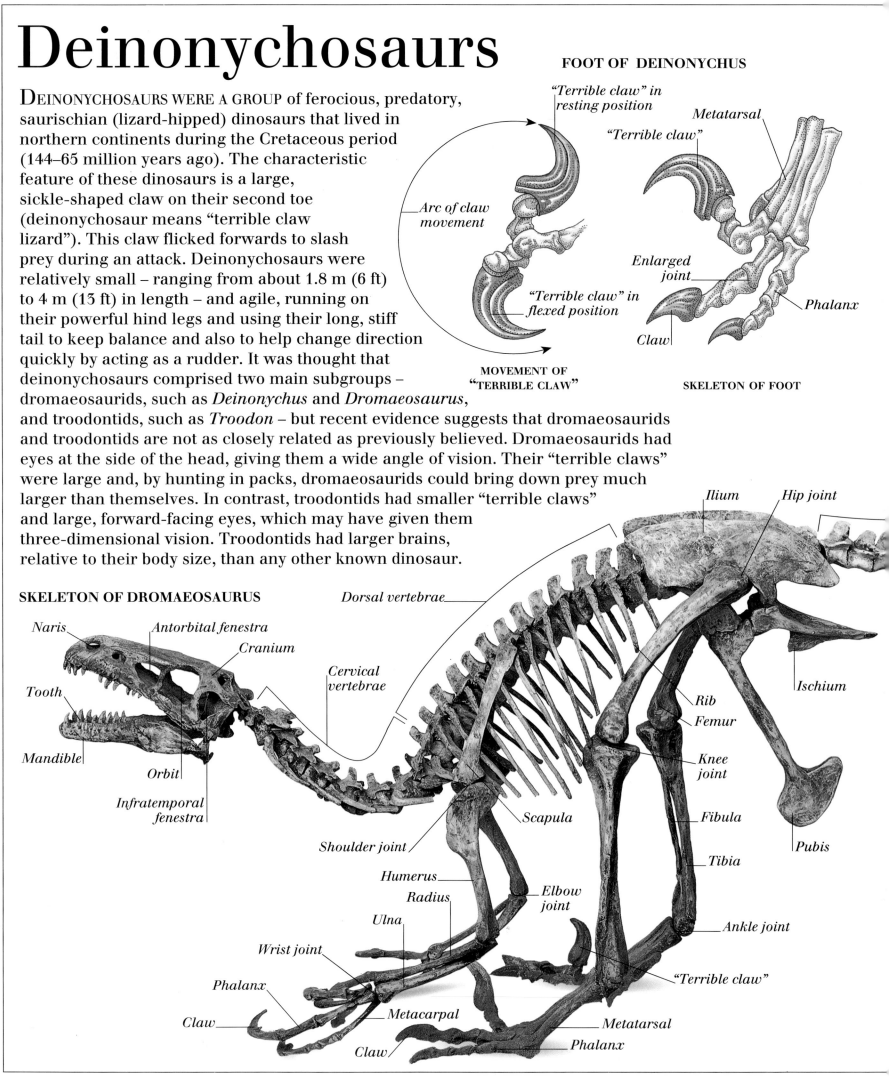

FOOT OF DEINONYCHUS

"Terrible claw" in resting position

"Terrible claw"

Metatarsal

Arc of claw movement

Enlarged joint

"Terrible claw" in flexed position

Phalanx

Claw

MOVEMENT OF "TERRIBLE CLAW"

SKELETON OF FOOT

SKELETON OF DROMAEOSAURUS

Ilium   *Hip joint*

Dorsal vertebrae

Naris

Antorbital fenestra

Cranium

Cervical vertebrae

Tooth

Ischium

Rib

Femur

Mandible

Orbit

Knee joint

Infratemporal fenestra

Scapula

Shoulder joint

Fibula

Humerus

Radius

Elbow joint

Pubis

Ulna

Tibia

Wrist joint

Ankle joint

Phalanx

Metatarsal

Claw

Metacarpal

"Terrible claw"

Phalanx

Claw

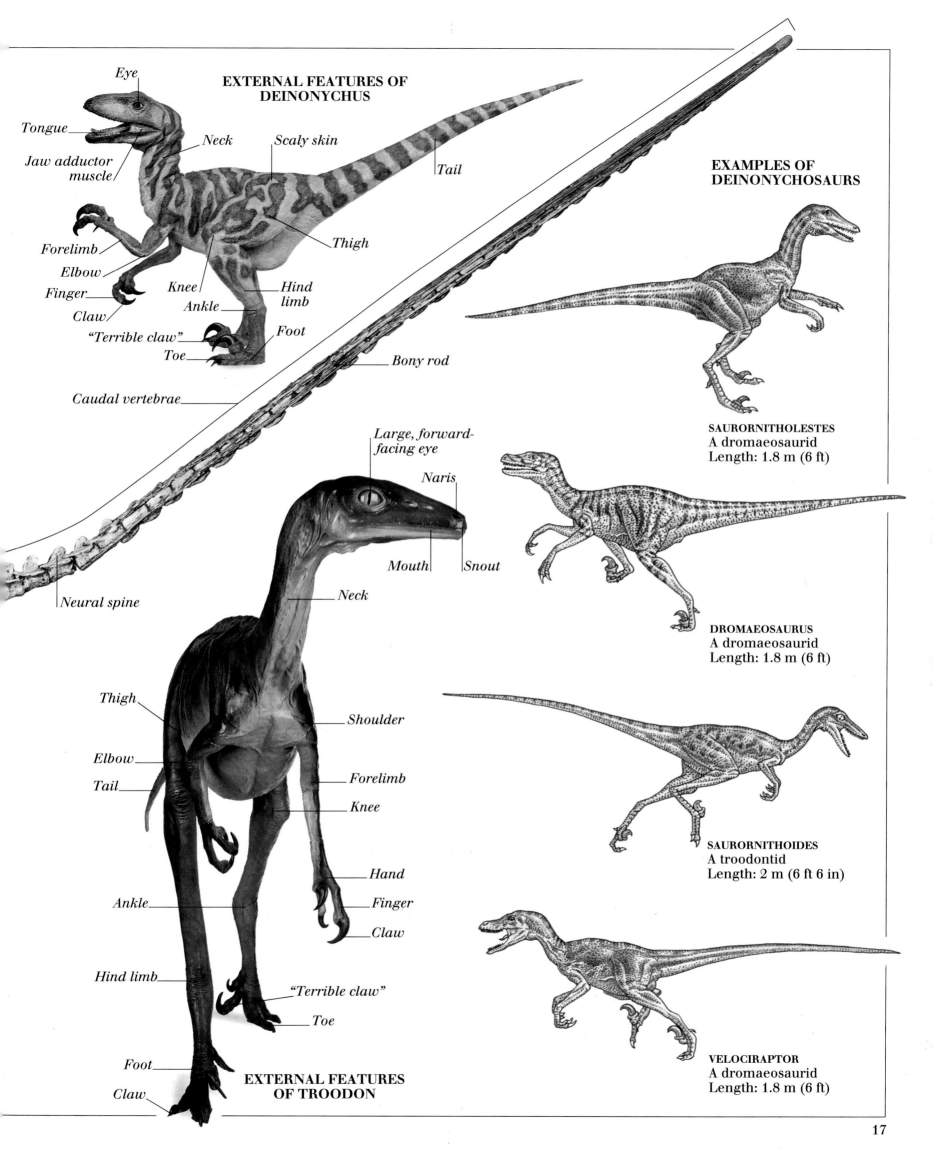

EXTERNAL FEATURES OF DEINONYCHUS

Eye

Tongue

Jaw adductor muscle

Neck

Scaly skin

Tail

Forelimb

Elbow

Finger

Claw

Thigh

Knee

Hind limb

Ankle

"Terrible claw"

Toe

Foot

Bony rod

Caudal vertebrae

Neural spine

EXAMPLES OF DEINONYCHOSAURS

SAURORNITHOLESTES
A dromaeosaurid
Length: 1.8 m (6 ft)

Large, forward-facing eye

Naris

Mouth

Snout

Neck

Thigh

Shoulder

Elbow

Forelimb

Tail

Knee

Hand

Finger

Claw

Ankle

Hind limb

"Terrible claw"

Toe

Foot

Claw

EXTERNAL FEATURES OF TROODON

DROMAEOSAURUS
A dromaeosaurid
Length: 1.8 m (6 ft)

SAURORNITHOIDES
A troodontid
Length: 2 m (6 ft 6 in)

VELOCIRAPTOR
A dromaeosaurid
Length: 1.8 m (6 ft)

17

Toothless theropods

TOOTHLESS THEROPODS COMPRISED TWO MAIN SUBGROUPS OF saurischian (lizard-hipped) dinosaurs: ornithomimosaurs and oviraptorosaurs. Both groups lived during Late Cretaceous times (97.5–65 million years ago) in what are now Asia, North America, and Africa. They had toothless beaks, in contrast to the small theropods (see pp. 14-15), which had jaws containing small, sharp teeth. Ornithomimosaurs (meaning "bird-mimic lizards"), such as *Gallimimus*, *Ornithomimus*, *Struthiomimus*, and *Dromiceiomimus*, had some features in common with the modern ostrich: a small head with a long, narrow beak, a long neck, and powerful hind limbs. Oviraptorosaurs (meaning "egg-plundering lizards"), such as *Oviraptor* (see p. 32), also had ostrich-like features, but their beaks were short. The internal anatomy of ornithomimosaurs and oviraptorosaurs is thought to have resembled that of modern birds, with a gizzard (muscular stomach) for grinding up food.

Eye

Toothless beak

Orbit

Cranium

Antorbital fenestra

Maxilla

Naris

Mandible

Mandibular fenestra

SKULL AND MANDIBLE OF DROMICEIOMIMUS

INTERNAL ANATOMY OF FEMALE GALLIMIMUS

Cervical musculature

Scapula

Lung

Gizzard

Rib

Dorsal vertebra

Ovary

Kidney

Ilium

Hip joint

Femur

Neural spine

Caudal vertebra

Trachea

Shoulder joint

Coracoid

Heart

Humerus

Posterior brachial muscle

Anterior brachial muscle

Claw

Anterior antebrachial muscle

Liver

Intestine

Posterior antebrachial muscle

Pubis

Ulna

Metacarpal

Femoral musculature

Anterior crural muscle

Chevron

Cloaca

Ischium

Posterior crural muscle

Fibula

Tibia

Tarsal

Metatarsal

Tendon

Phalanx

Toothless beak

Neck

Scaly skin

Tail

Elbow

Hand

Ankle

Foot

Claw

EXTERNAL FEATURES OF GALLIMIMUS

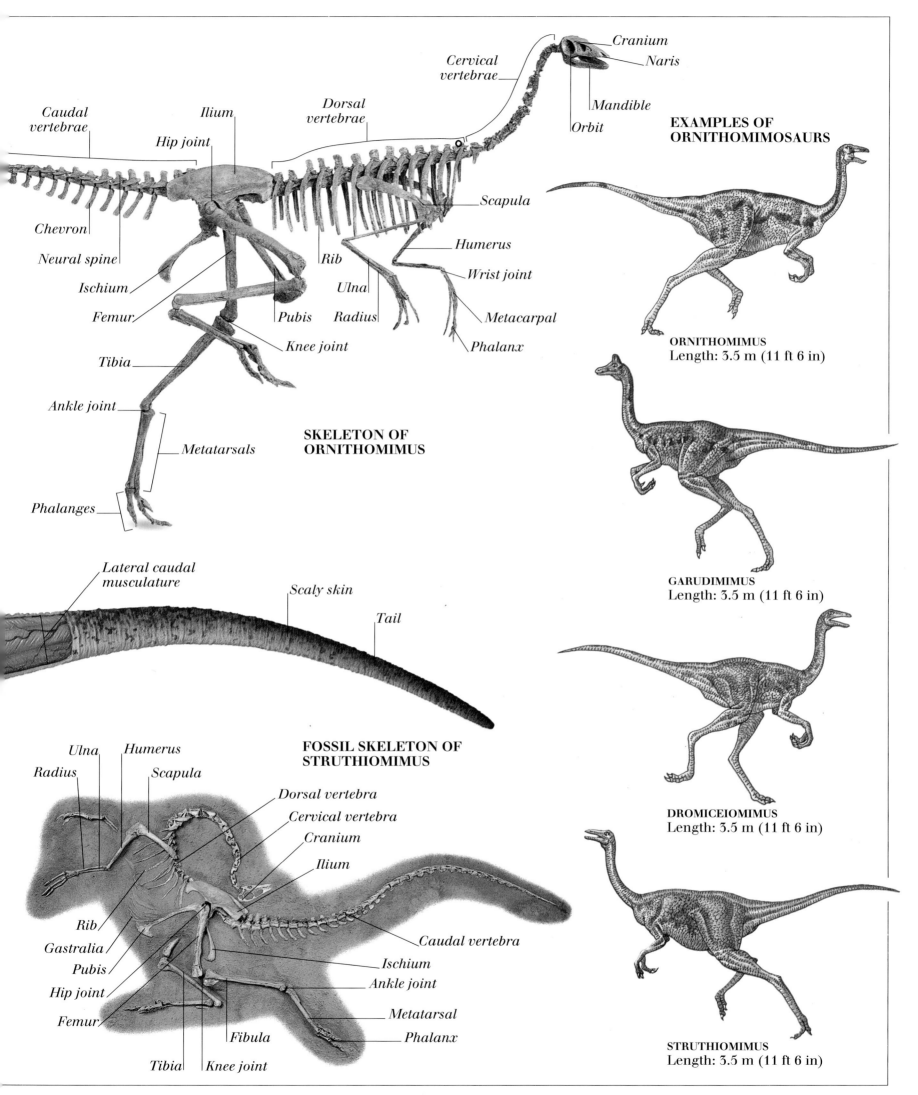

Caudal
vertebrae

Ilium

Dorsal
vertebrae

Cervical
vertebrae

Cranium

Naris

Hip joint

Mandible

Orbit

**EXAMPLES OF
ORNITHOMIMOSAURS**

Chevron

Neural spine

Ischium

Scapula

Femur

Rib

Humerus

Pubis

Ulna

Wrist joint

Radius

Metacarpal

Knee joint

Phalanx

ORNITHOMIMUS
Length: 3.5 m (11 ft 6 in)

Tibia

Ankle joint

Metatarsals

**SKELETON OF
ORNITHOMIMUS**

Phalanges

Lateral caudal
musculature

Scaly skin

GARUDIMIMUS
Length: 3.5 m (11 ft 6 in)

Tail

Ulna

Humerus

**FOSSIL SKELETON OF
STRUTHIOMIMUS**

Radius

Scapula

Dorsal vertebra

Cervical vertebra

Cranium

Ilium

Rib

Caudal vertebra

DROMICEIOMIMUS
Length: 3.5 m (11 ft 6 in)

Gastralia

Ischium

Pubis

Hip joint

Ankle joint

Femur

Metatarsal

Phalanx

Fibula

Tibia

Knee joint

STRUTHIOMIMUS
Length: 3.5 m (11 ft 6 in)

Carnosaurs 1

CARNOSAURS IS A TERM OFTEN USED loosely for the Carnosauria and other large flesh-eating, saurischian (lizard-hipped) dinosaurs, such as *Carnotaurus* (a large ceratosaur). Carnosaurs ranged in size from 6.1 m (20 ft) to 15.2 m (50 ft) in length, and weighed up to about 6.4 tonnes (6.3 tons). As a group, carnosaurs were very successful; they lived from Early Jurassic to Late Cretaceous times (208–65 million years ago) and their fossils have been discovered throughout the world. Typical carnosaurs, such as *Tyrannosaurus* and *Allosaurus*, had large heads; short, muscular necks; powerful hind legs; and stiff, heavy tails to aid balance. They probably hunted herbivores (plant-eaters) and were the most formidable of all predatory dinosaurs, with jaws that could have swallowed a human, and curved, serrated teeth up to 18 cm (7 in) long for ripping flesh from their prey. Some carnosaurs had unusual features; for example, *Spinosaurus* – at 15.2 m (50 ft) the largest carnosaur yet discovered – had a 1.5 m (5 ft) tall "sail" along its back. The exact function of this sail is not known, but it may have been used to regulate body temperature, attract mates, or intimidate other dinosaurs during territorial battles. Another unusual carnosaur was *Baryonyx*, whose long neck, crocodile-like jaws with many sharp teeth, and relatively long forelimbs with large hooked claws were probably adapted for hunting fish.

BARYONYX CLAW

MODEL OF BARYONYX IN DEATH POSITION

Crocodile-like jaw

Neck

Shoulder

Thigh

Tail

Ankle

Foot

Hind limb

Knee

Hind limb

Forelimb

Wrist

Hand

Tail

Scaly skin

EXTERNAL FEATURES OF BARYONYX

Long neck

Eye

Naris

Sharp tooth

Tongue

Forelimb

Elbow

Wrist

Hand

Finger

Hooked thumb-claw

Finger-claw

Thigh

Ankle

Knee

Foot

Hind limb

Hallux (first toe)

Toe

Toe-claw

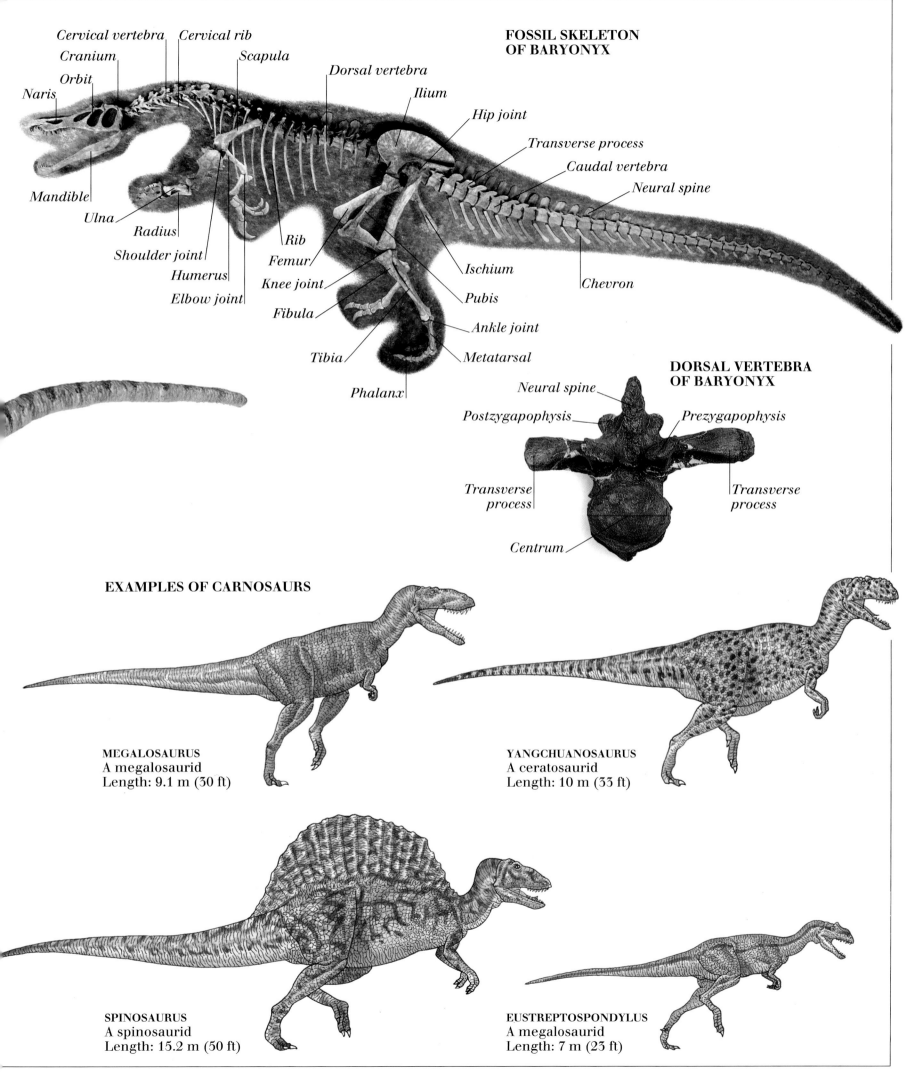

FOSSIL SKELETON OF BARYONYX

Cervical vertebra
Cervical rib
Cranium
Orbit
Naris
Scapula
Dorsal vertebra
Ilium
Hip joint
Transverse process
Caudal vertebra
Neural spine
Mandible
Ulna
Radius
Shoulder joint
Humerus
Elbow joint
Rib
Femur
Knee joint
Fibula
Tibia
Phalanx
Ischium
Pubis
Ankle joint
Metatarsal
Chevron

DORSAL VERTEBRA OF BARYONYX

Neural spine
Postzygapophysis
Prezygapophysis
Transverse process
Transverse process
Centrum

EXAMPLES OF CARNOSAURS

MEGALOSAURUS
A megalosaurid
Length: 9.1 m (30 ft)

YANGCHUANOSAURUS
A ceratosaurid
Length: 10 m (33 ft)

SPINOSAURUS
A spinosaurid
Length: 15.2 m (50 ft)

EUSTREPTOSPONDYLUS
A megalosaurid
Length: 7 m (23 ft)

Carnosaurs 2

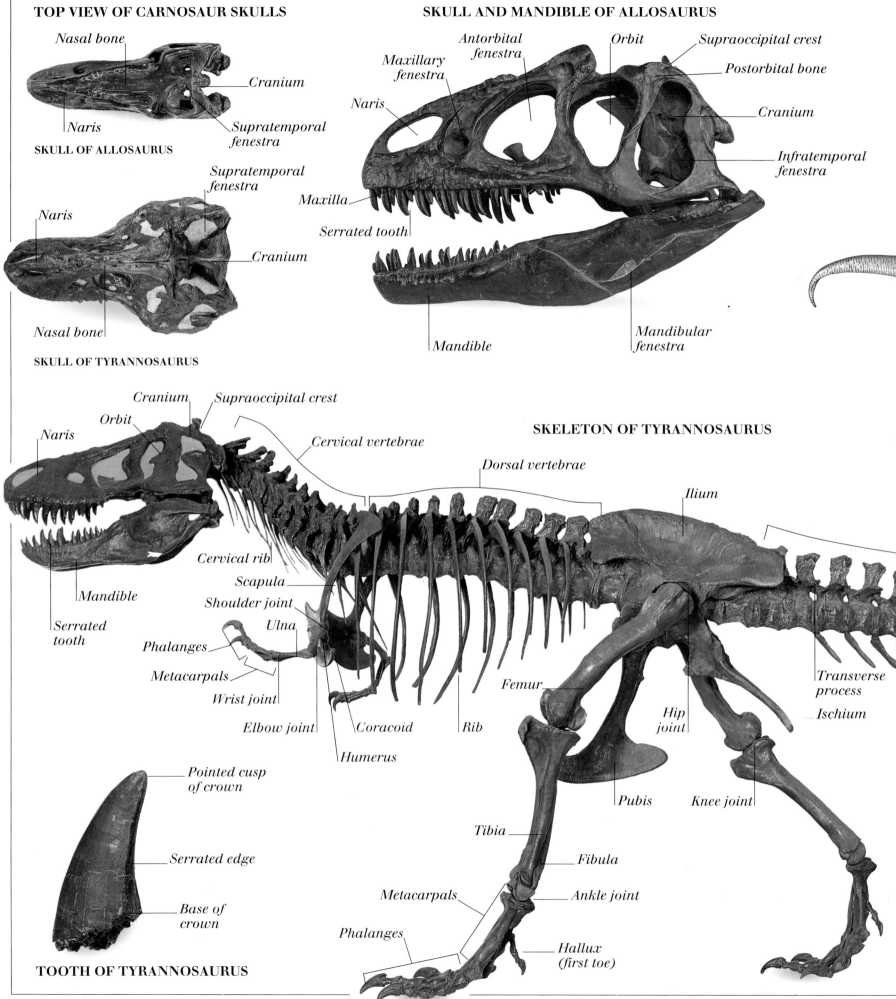

TOP VIEW OF CARNOSAUR SKULLS

Nasal bone

Naris

Cranium

Supratemporal fenestra

SKULL OF ALLOSAURUS

Naris

Supratemporal fenestra

Cranium

Nasal bone

SKULL OF TYRANNOSAURUS

SKULL AND MANDIBLE OF ALLOSAURUS

Maxillary fenestra

Antorbital fenestra

Orbit

Supraoccipital crest

Postorbital bone

Naris

Cranium

Infratemporal fenestra

Maxilla

Serrated tooth

Mandible

Mandibular fenestra

SKELETON OF TYRANNOSAURUS

Cranium

Orbit

Supraoccipital crest

Naris

Cervical vertebrae

Dorsal vertebrae

Ilium

Cervical rib

Scapula

Shoulder joint

Ulna

Phalanges

Metacarpals

Wrist joint

Elbow joint

Humerus

Coracoid

Rib

Mandible

Serrated tooth

Femur

Hip joint

Transverse process

Ischium

Pubis

Knee joint

Tibia

Fibula

Metacarpals

Ankle joint

Phalanges

Hallux (first toe)

Pointed cusp of crown

Serrated edge

Base of crown

TOOTH OF TYRANNOSAURUS

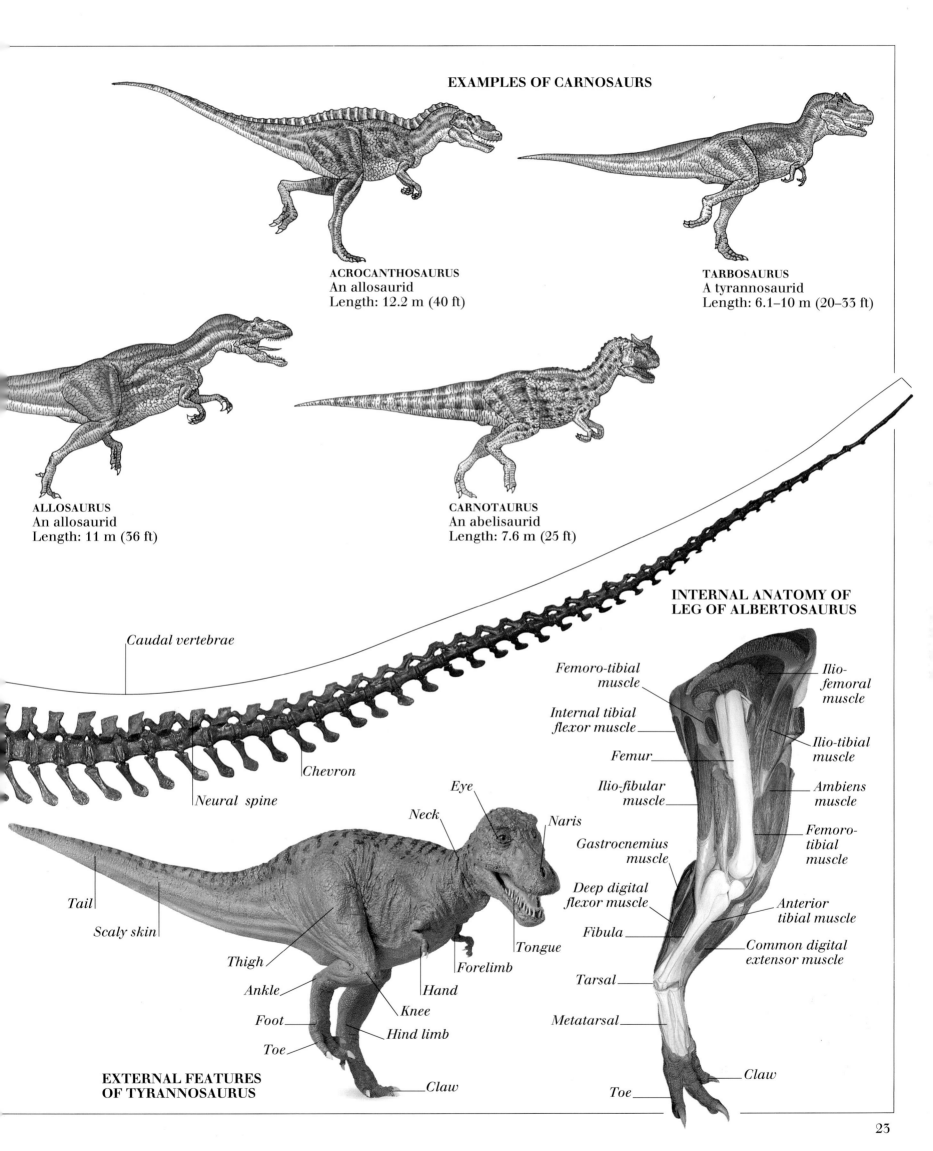

EXAMPLES OF CARNOSAURS

ACROCANTHOSAURUS
An allosaurid
Length: 12.2 m (40 ft)

TARBOSAURUS
A tyrannosaurid
Length: 6.1–10 m (20–33 ft)

ALLOSAURUS
An allosaurid
Length: 11 m (36 ft)

CARNOTAURUS
An abelisaurid
Length: 7.6 m (25 ft)

Caudal vertebrae

Chevron

Neural spine

INTERNAL ANATOMY OF LEG OF ALBERTOSAURUS

Femoro-tibial muscle

Internal tibial flexor muscle

Femur

Ilio-fibular muscle

Gastrocnemius muscle

Deep digital flexor muscle

Fibula

Tarsal

Metatarsal

Ilio-femoral muscle

Ilio-tibial muscle

Ambiens muscle

Femoro-tibial muscle

Anterior tibial muscle

Common digital extensor muscle

Toe

Claw

Eye

Neck

Naris

Tongue

Forelimb

Hand

Tail

Scaly skin

Thigh

Ankle

Foot

Knee

Hind limb

Toe

Claw

EXTERNAL FEATURES OF TYRANNOSAURUS

Prosauropods

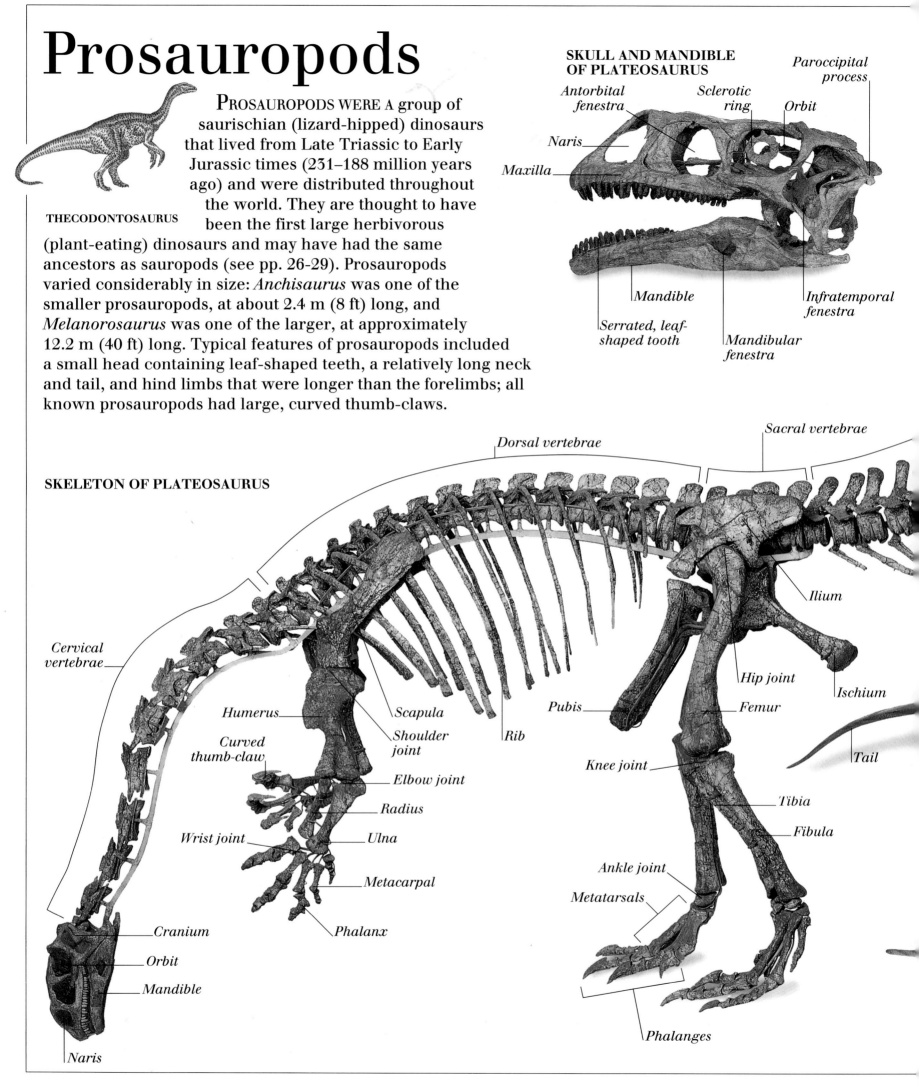

PROSAUROPODS WERE A group of saurischian (lizard-hipped) dinosaurs that lived from Late Triassic to Early Jurassic times (231–188 million years ago) and were distributed throughout the world. They are thought to have been the first large herbivorous (plant-eating) dinosaurs and may have had the same ancestors as sauropods (see pp. 26-29). Prosauropods varied considerably in size: *Anchisaurus* was one of the smaller prosauropods, at about 2.4 m (8 ft) long, and *Melanorosaurus* was one of the larger, at approximately 12.2 m (40 ft) long. Typical features of prosauropods included a small head containing leaf-shaped teeth, a relatively long neck and tail, and hind limbs that were longer than the forelimbs; all known prosauropods had large, curved thumb-claws.

THECODONTOSAURUS

SKULL AND MANDIBLE OF PLATEOSAURUS

Antorbital fenestra
Sclerotic ring
Paroccipital process
Orbit
Naris
Maxilla
Mandible
Serrated, leaf-shaped tooth
Mandibular fenestra
Infratemporal fenestra

SKELETON OF PLATEOSAURUS

Dorsal vertebrae
Sacral vertebrae
Ilium
Cervical vertebrae
Hip joint
Ischium
Pubis
Femur
Tail
Humerus
Scapula
Rib
Curved thumb-claw
Shoulder joint
Knee joint
Elbow joint
Tibia
Radius
Fibula
Wrist joint
Ulna
Ankle joint
Metacarpal
Metatarsals
Cranium
Phalanx
Orbit
Mandible
Phalanges
Naris

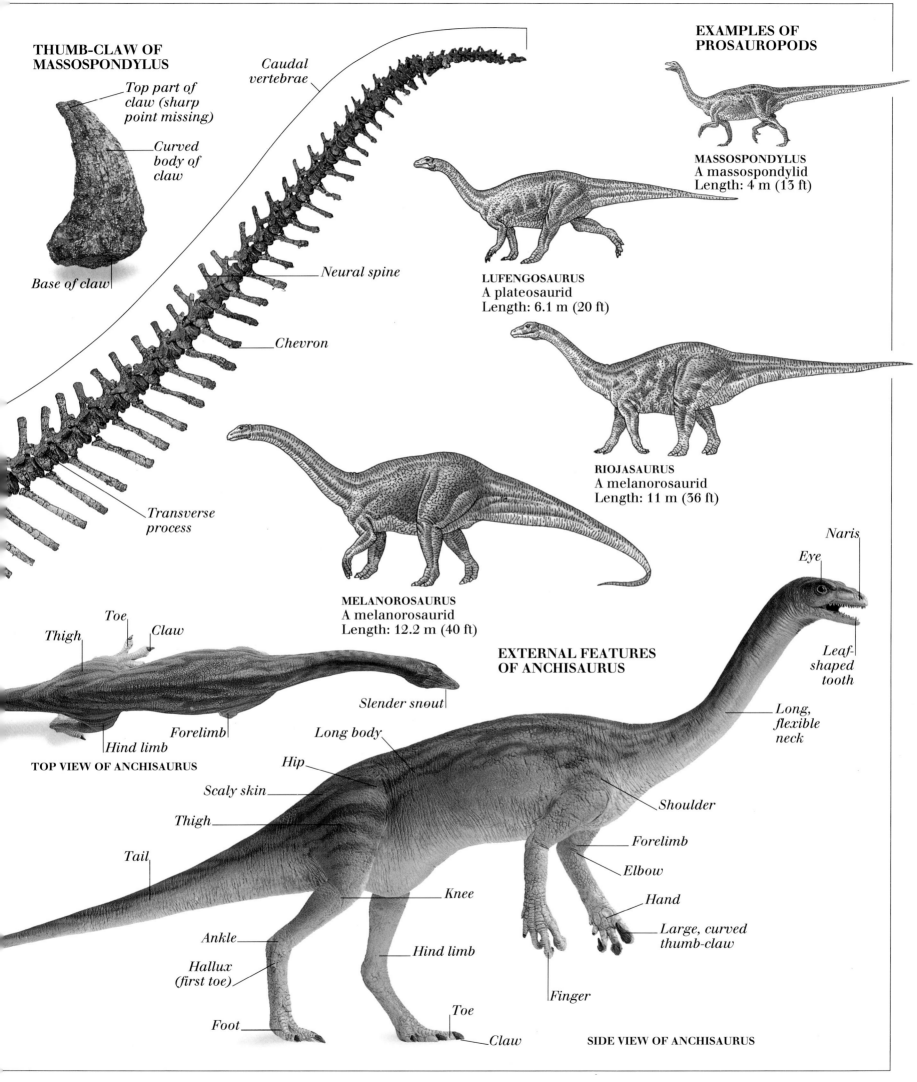

THUMB-CLAW OF MASSOSPONDYLUS

Top part of claw (sharp point missing)

Curved body of claw

Base of claw

Caudal vertebrae

Neural spine

Chevron

Transverse process

EXAMPLES OF PROSAUROPODS

MASSOSPONDYLUS
A massospondylid
Length: 4 m (13 ft)

LUFENGOSAURUS
A plateosaurid
Length: 6.1 m (20 ft)

RIOJASAURUS
A melanorosaurid
Length: 11 m (36 ft)

MELANOROSAURUS
A melanorosaurid
Length: 12.2 m (40 ft)

Toe
Thigh
Claw

Slender snout

Forelimb
Hind limb

TOP VIEW OF ANCHISAURUS

EXTERNAL FEATURES OF ANCHISAURUS

Naris
Eye
Leaf-shaped tooth

Long, flexible neck

Long body
Hip
Scaly skin
Thigh

Shoulder

Forelimb
Elbow
Hand

Large, curved thumb-claw

Tail
Knee
Ankle
Hallux (first toe)
Hind limb
Foot
Toe
Claw
Finger

SIDE VIEW OF ANCHISAURUS

Sauropods 1

SAUROPODS FORMED A large group of saurischian (lizard-hipped) dinosaurs that included some of the largest animals ever to have lived. *Brachiosaurus* was one of the heaviest, weighing up to 77 tonnes (75 tons), which is more than the weight of 10 elephants. *Diplodocus* was one of the longest sauropods; measuring about 27.4 m (90 ft) from head to tail, it was almost as long as a blue whale, which, at about 30 m (100 ft), is the longest living animal. Sauropods supported their massive weight on pillar-like legs, which probably resembled those of elephants (see p. 28). As a group, sauropods were among the most successful dinosaurs: they existed from Early Jurassic to Late Cretaceous times (208–65 million years ago) and were found throughout the world. As well as being huge, sauropods typically had small heads; long, flexible necks; bulky bodies; and long tails. Some sauropods' bones were honeycombed with pleurocoels (hollows) to minimize weight. Sauropods were herbivores and, being so large, needed to eat vast amounts of vegetation. Consequently, their long necks – up to 14.9 m (49 ft) long in the case of *Mamenchisaurus* – were a great advantage, enabling them to reach vegetation that was too high up for other dinosaurs. Sauropods had no grinding teeth, which suggests that they swallowed food without chewing it; instead, it was probably ground up by gastroliths (stones) in the gizzard (muscular stomach).

GASTROLITHS (GIZZARD STONES)

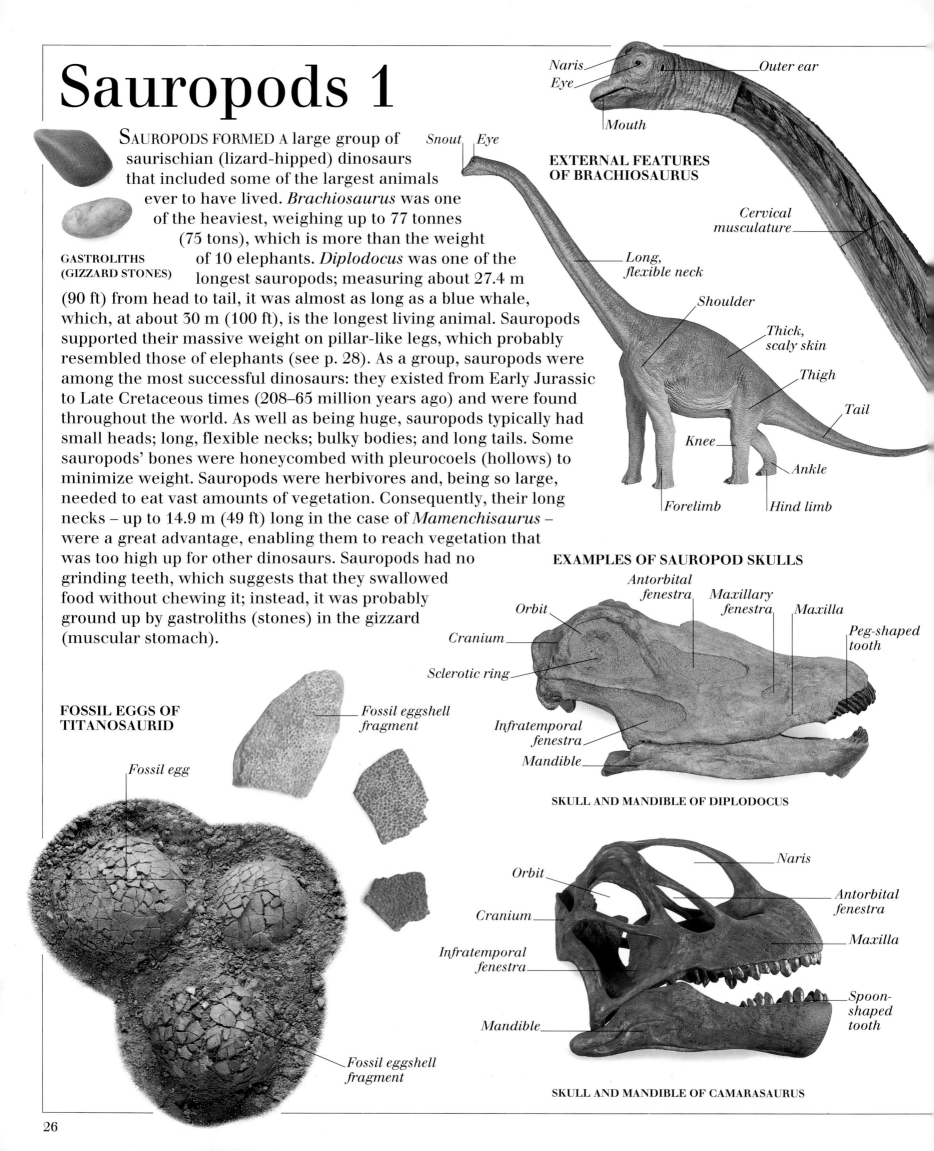

EXTERNAL FEATURES OF BRACHIOSAURUS

Naris
Eye
Outer ear
Mouth
Snout
Eye
Cervical musculature
Long, flexible neck
Shoulder
Thick, scaly skin
Thigh
Tail
Knee
Ankle
Forelimb
Hind limb

EXAMPLES OF SAUROPOD SKULLS

Antorbital fenestra
Maxillary fenestra
Maxilla
Orbit
Cranium
Peg-shaped tooth
Sclerotic ring
Infratemporal fenestra
Mandible

SKULL AND MANDIBLE OF DIPLODOCUS

FOSSIL EGGS OF TITANOSAURID

Fossil eggshell fragment

Fossil egg

Naris
Orbit
Antorbital fenestra
Cranium
Maxilla
Infratemporal fenestra
Mandible
Spoon-shaped tooth

SKULL AND MANDIBLE OF CAMARASAURUS

Fossil eggshell fragment

26

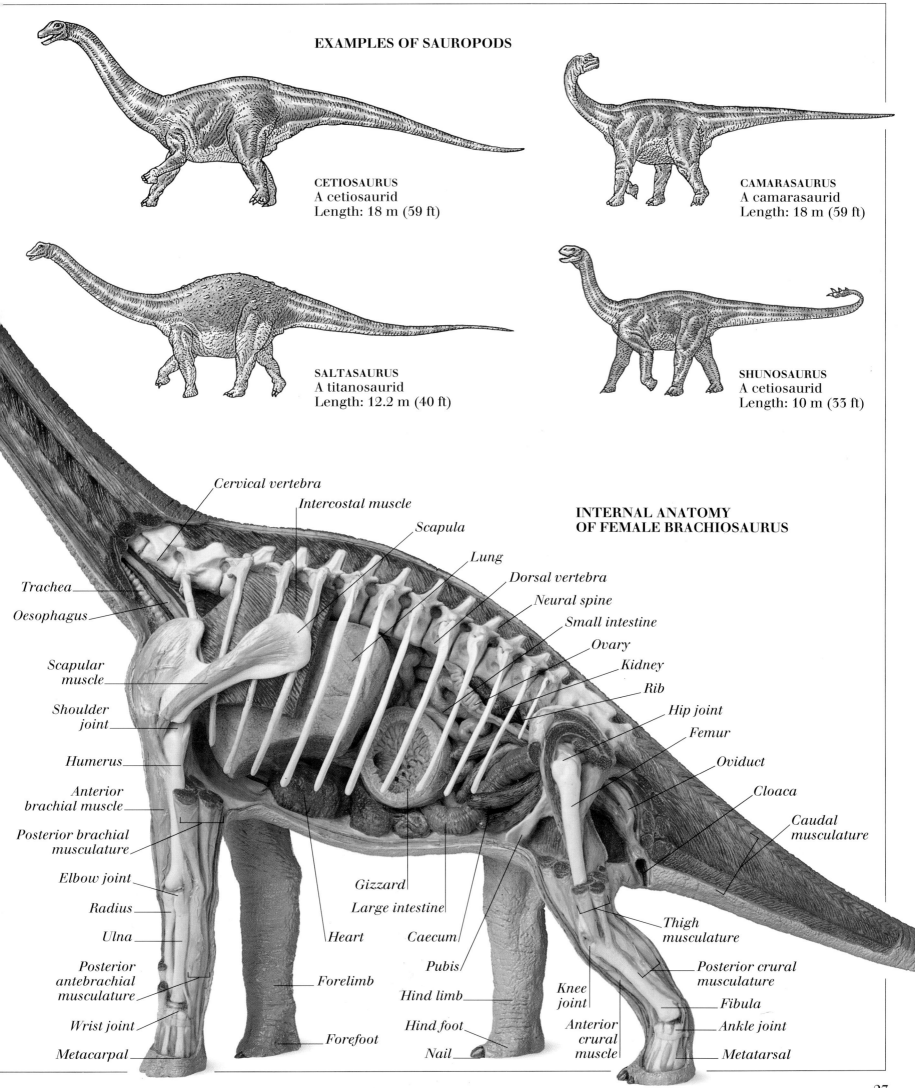

EXAMPLES OF SAUROPODS

CETIOSAURUS
A cetiosaurid
Length: 18 m (59 ft)

CAMARASAURUS
A camarasaurid
Length: 18 m (59 ft)

SALTASAURUS
A titanosaurid
Length: 12.2 m (40 ft)

SHUNOSAURUS
A cetiosaurid
Length: 10 m (33 ft)

INTERNAL ANATOMY OF FEMALE BRACHIOSAURUS

Cervical vertebra
Intercostal muscle
Scapula
Lung
Dorsal vertebra
Neural spine
Small intestine
Ovary
Kidney
Rib
Hip joint
Femur
Oviduct
Cloaca
Caudal musculature

Trachea
Oesophagus
Scapular muscle
Shoulder joint
Humerus
Anterior brachial muscle
Posterior brachial musculature
Elbow joint
Radius
Ulna
Posterior antebrachial musculature
Wrist joint
Metacarpal

Gizzard
Large intestine
Heart
Caecum
Pubis
Hind limb
Hind foot
Nail
Forelimb
Forefoot

Thigh musculature
Knee joint
Anterior crural muscle
Posterior crural musculature
Fibula
Ankle joint
Metatarsal

Sauropods 2

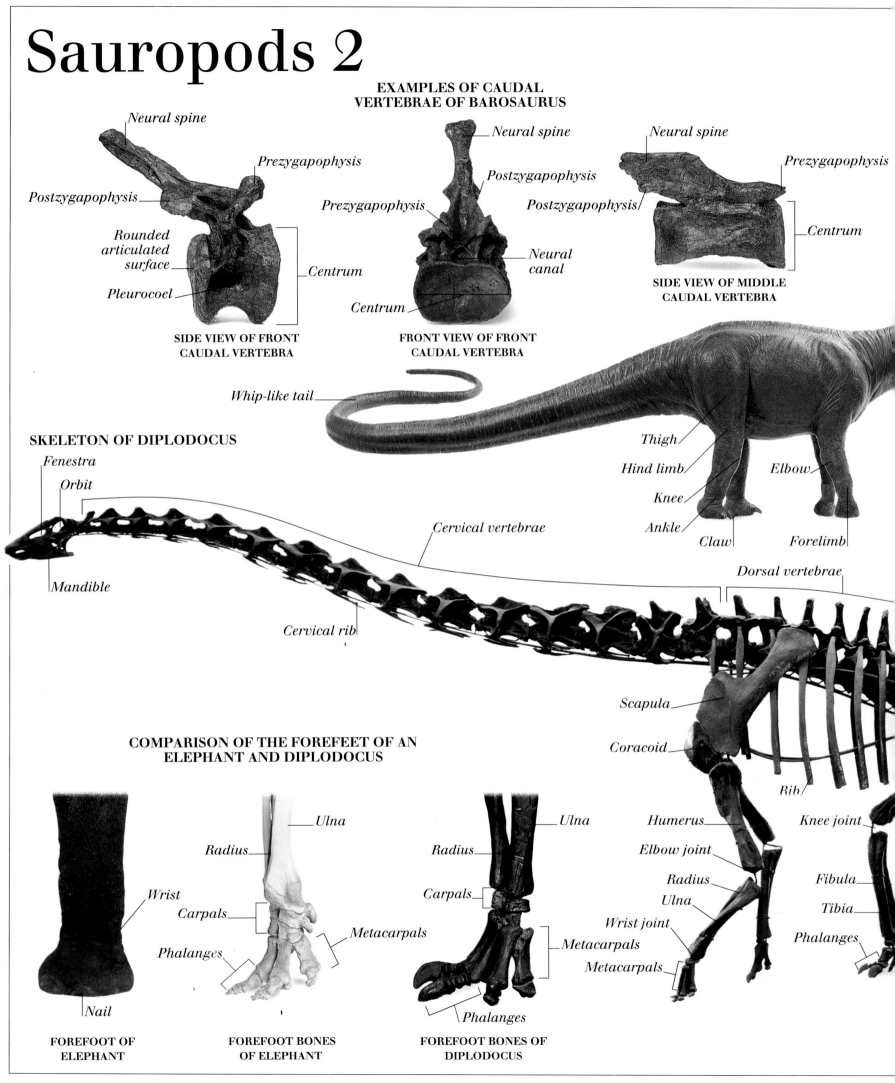

EXAMPLES OF CAUDAL VERTEBRAE OF BAROSAURUS

Neural spine

Postzygapophysis

Prezygapophysis

Rounded articulated surface

Pleurocoel

Centrum

SIDE VIEW OF FRONT CAUDAL VERTEBRA

Neural spine

Postzygapophysis

Prezygapophysis

Neural canal

Centrum

FRONT VIEW OF FRONT CAUDAL VERTEBRA

Neural spine

Prezygapophysis

Postzygapophysis

Centrum

SIDE VIEW OF MIDDLE CAUDAL VERTEBRA

Whip-like tail

Thigh

Hind limb

Knee

Ankle

Claw

Elbow

Forelimb

SKELETON OF DIPLODOCUS

Fenestra

Orbit

Mandible

Cervical vertebrae

Cervical rib

Dorsal vertebrae

Scapula

Coracoid

Rib

Humerus

Knee joint

Elbow joint

Radius

Ulna

Wrist joint

Fibula

Tibia

Phalanges

Metacarpals

Metacarpals

COMPARISON OF THE FOREFEET OF AN ELEPHANT AND DIPLODOCUS

Wrist

Phalanges

Nail

Ulna

Radius

Carpals

Metacarpals

Ulna

Radius

Carpals

Metacarpals

Phalanges

FOREFOOT OF ELEPHANT

FOREFOOT BONES OF ELEPHANT

FOREFOOT BONES OF DIPLODOCUS

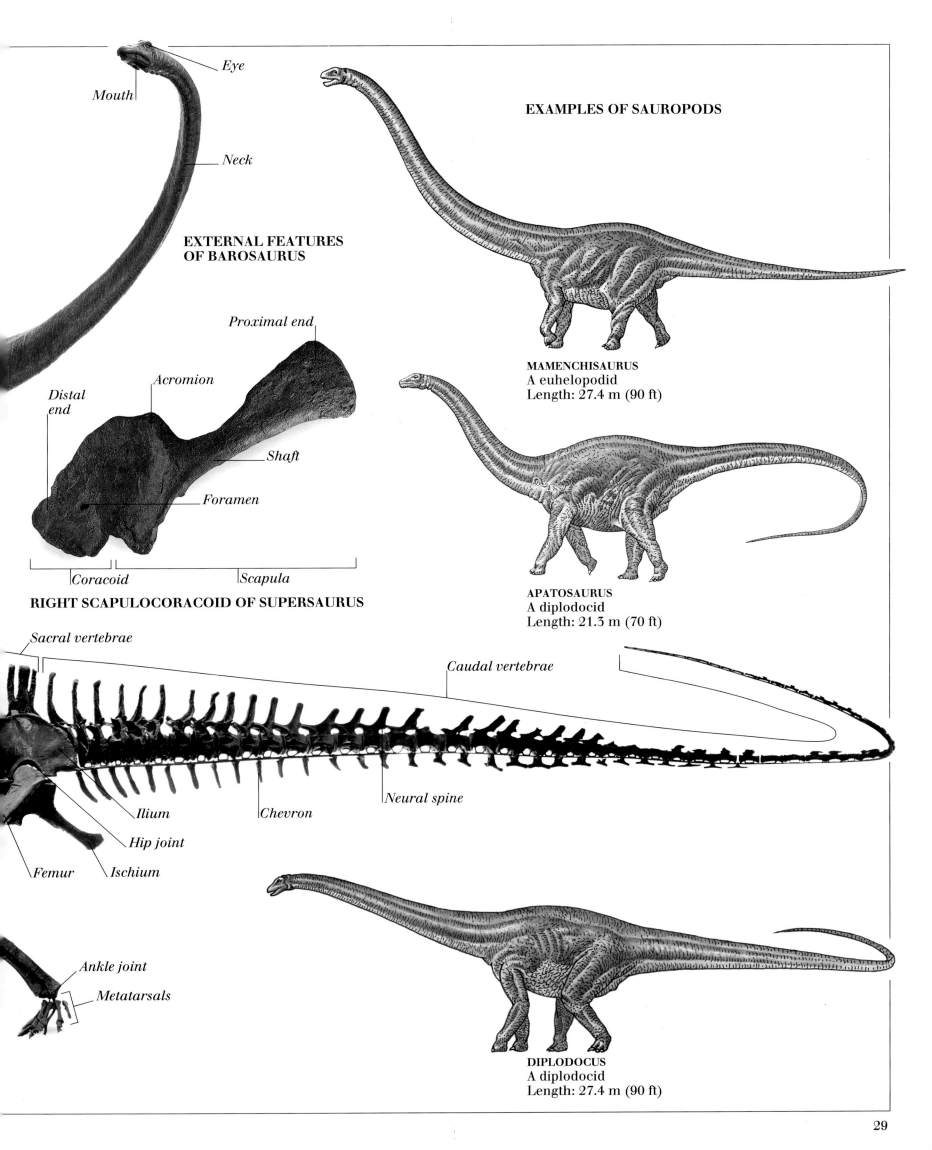

Eye

Mouth

**EXTERNAL FEATURES
OF BAROSAURUS**

Neck

EXAMPLES OF SAUROPODS

Proximal end

Acromion

Distal
end

Shaft

Foramen

Coracoid

Scapula

RIGHT SCAPULOCORACOID OF SUPERSAURUS

MAMENCHISAURUS
A euhelopodid
Length: 27.4 m (90 ft)

APATOSAURUS
A diplodocid
Length: 21.3 m (70 ft)

Sacral vertebrae

Caudal vertebrae

Neural spine

Ilium

Chevron

Hip joint

Femur   Ischium

Ankle joint

Metatarsals

DIPLODOCUS
A diplodocid
Length: 27.4 m (90 ft)

29

Herbivores' heads

HEAD OF GALLIMIMUS

HERBIVOROUS (PLANT-EATING) DINOSAURS spent much of their time eating. The wide range of vegetation consumed by the various herbivores is reflected in the diversity of their heads, particularly of their jaws and teeth. For example, *Gallimimus* had a beak for cropping fruit and vegetation; *Anchisaurus* had ridged teeth for shredding the leaves from plants; *Stegosaurus* had a beak, and cheek teeth for grinding vegetation; and *Triceratops* had batteries of cheek teeth for slicing up plant food. The jaws of some herbivorous dinosaurs could move from side to side, which enabled them to grind up vegetation in their mouths. Other herbivores relied on gastroliths (stones) in their gizzard (muscular stomach) to break up the vegetation they had eaten. Most herbivorous dinosaurs had eyes at the sides of their heads, giving them a wide angle of vision so that they could spot predators approaching from any direction. Some herbivores had distinctive features on their heads. For example, *Triceratops* had massive brow horns, possibly for use in territorial battles, and hadrosaurs, such as *Brachylophosaurus*, had crests that distinguished one species from another within a herd.

SAUROPOD TEETH

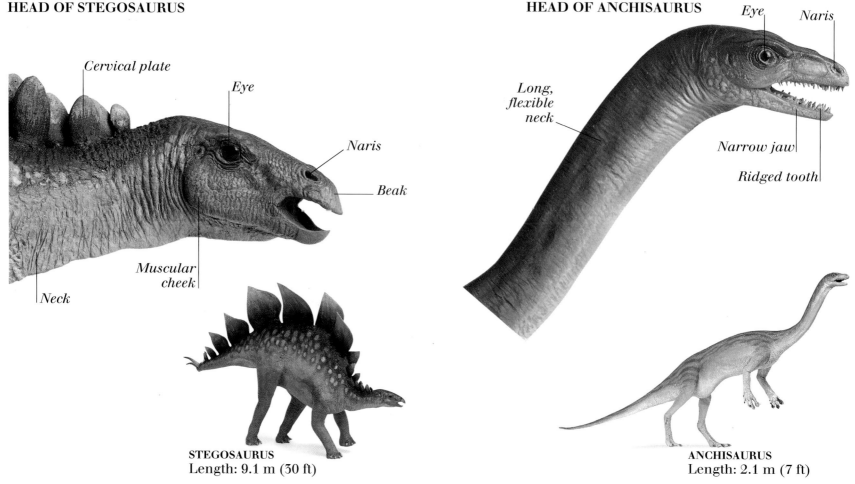

Eye

Naris

Jaw adductor muscle

Tongue

Toothless beak

Long, flexible neck

GALLIMIMUS
Length: 6.1 m (20 ft)

HEAD OF STEGOSAURUS

Cervical plate

Eye

Naris

Beak

Muscular cheek

Neck

STEGOSAURUS
Length: 9.1 m (30 ft)

HEAD OF ANCHISAURUS

Eye

Naris

Long, flexible neck

Narrow jaw

Ridged tooth

ANCHISAURUS
Length: 2.1 m (7 ft)

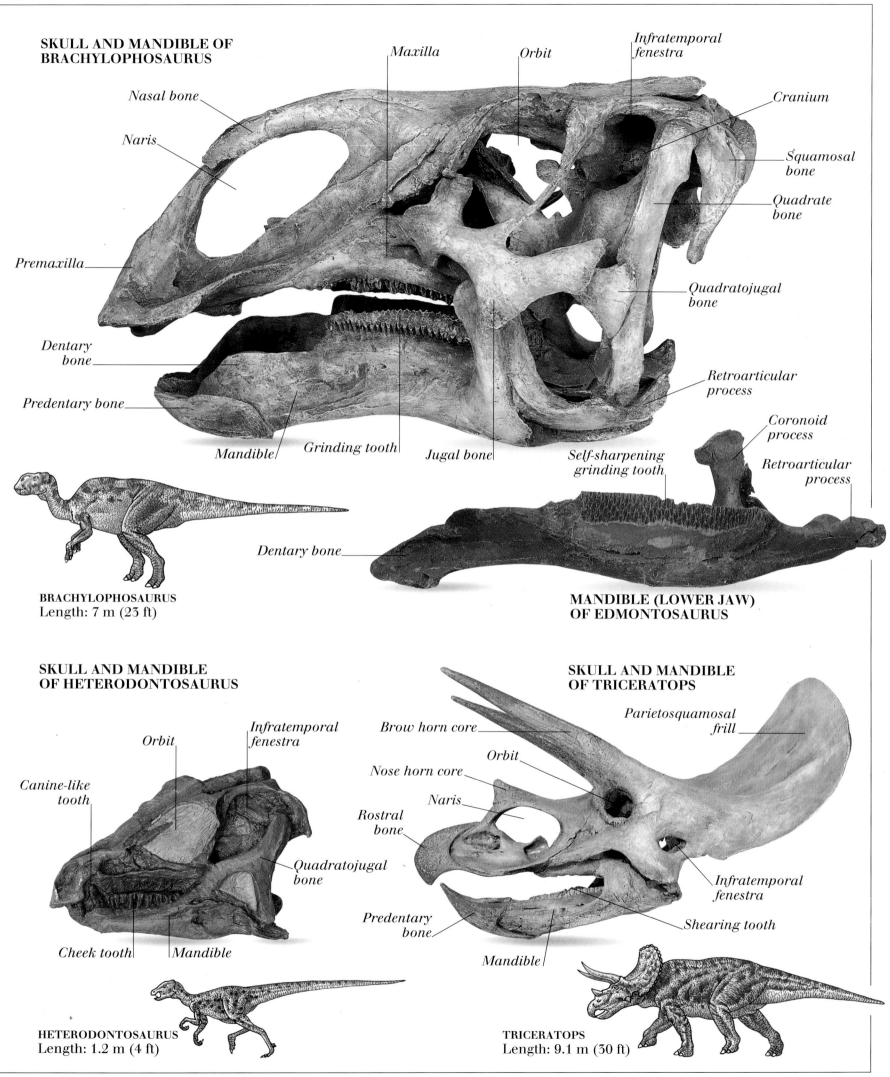

SKULL AND MANDIBLE OF BRACHYLOPHOSAURUS

Nasal bone

Naris

Premaxilla

Dentary bone

Predentary bone

Mandible

Grinding tooth

Maxilla

Orbit

Jugal bone

Infratemporal fenestra

Cranium

Squamosal bone

Quadrate bone

Quadratojugal bone

Retroarticular process

BRACHYLOPHOSAURUS
Length: 7 m (23 ft)

Self-sharpening grinding tooth

Coronoid process

Retroarticular process

Dentary bone

MANDIBLE (LOWER JAW) OF EDMONTOSAURUS

SKULL AND MANDIBLE OF HETERODONTOSAURUS

Orbit

Infratemporal fenestra

Canine-like tooth

Quadratojugal bone

Cheek tooth

Mandible

HETERODONTOSAURUS
Length: 1.2 m (4 ft)

SKULL AND MANDIBLE OF TRICERATOPS

Brow horn core

Nose horn core

Naris

Rostral bone

Predentary bone

Mandible

Parietosquamosal frill

Orbit

Infratemporal fenestra

Shearing tooth

TRICERATOPS
Length: 9.1 m (30 ft)

Carnivores' heads

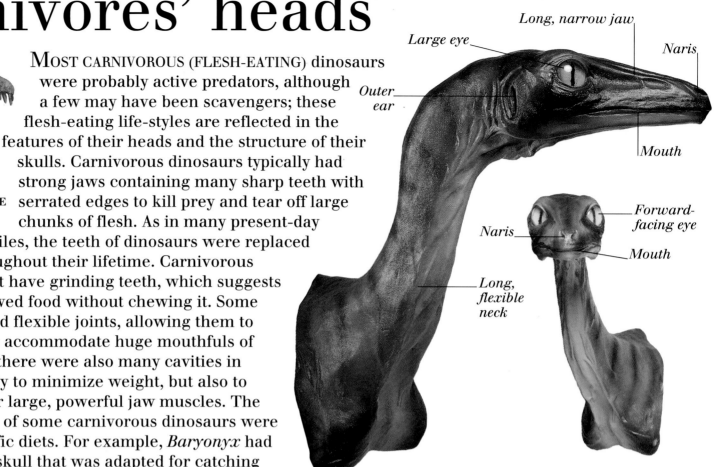

SKULL AND MANDIBLE OF DILOPHOSAURUS

MOST CARNIVOROUS (FLESH-EATING) dinosaurs were probably active predators, although a few may have been scavengers; these flesh-eating life-styles are reflected in the features of their heads and the structure of their skulls. Carnivorous dinosaurs typically had strong jaws containing many sharp teeth with serrated edges to kill prey and tear off large chunks of flesh. As in many present-day carnivorous reptiles, the teeth of dinosaurs were replaced continually throughout their lifetime. Carnivorous dinosaurs did not have grinding teeth, which suggests that they swallowed food without chewing it. Some of their skulls had flexible joints, allowing them to distort slightly to accommodate huge mouthfuls of flesh. Typically, there were also many cavities in the skull, not only to minimize weight, but also to provide space for large, powerful jaw muscles. The heads and skulls of some carnivorous dinosaurs were adapted to specific diets. For example, *Baryonyx* had a crocodile-like skull that was adapted for catching fish, whereas *Oviraptor* had a deep, strong beak that was adapted for breaking into the shells of eggs or molluscs.

Large eye · Long, narrow jaw · Naris · Outer ear · Mouth · Naris · Forward-facing eye · Mouth · Long, flexible neck

HEAD OF TROODON

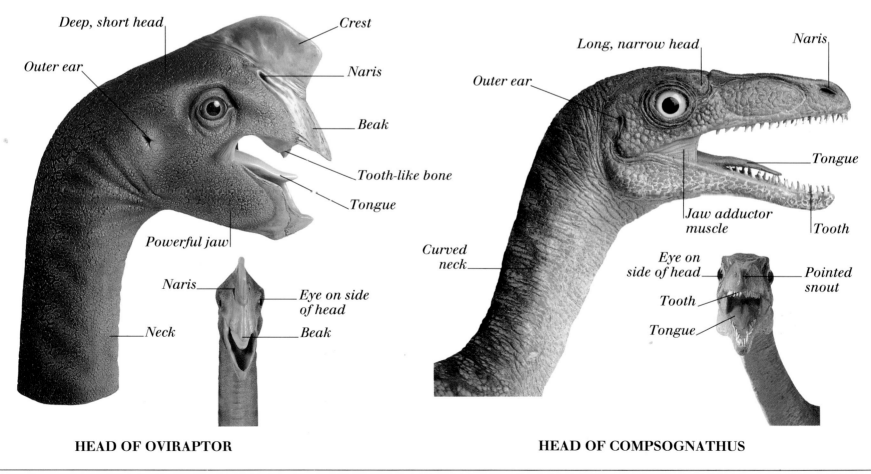

Deep, short head · Crest · Outer ear · Naris · Beak · Tooth-like bone · Tongue · Powerful jaw · Naris · Eye on side of head · Neck · Beak

HEAD OF OVIRAPTOR

Long, narrow head · Naris · Outer ear · Tongue · Jaw adductor muscle · Tooth · Curved neck · Eye on side of head · Pointed snout · Tooth · Tongue

HEAD OF COMPSOGNATHUS

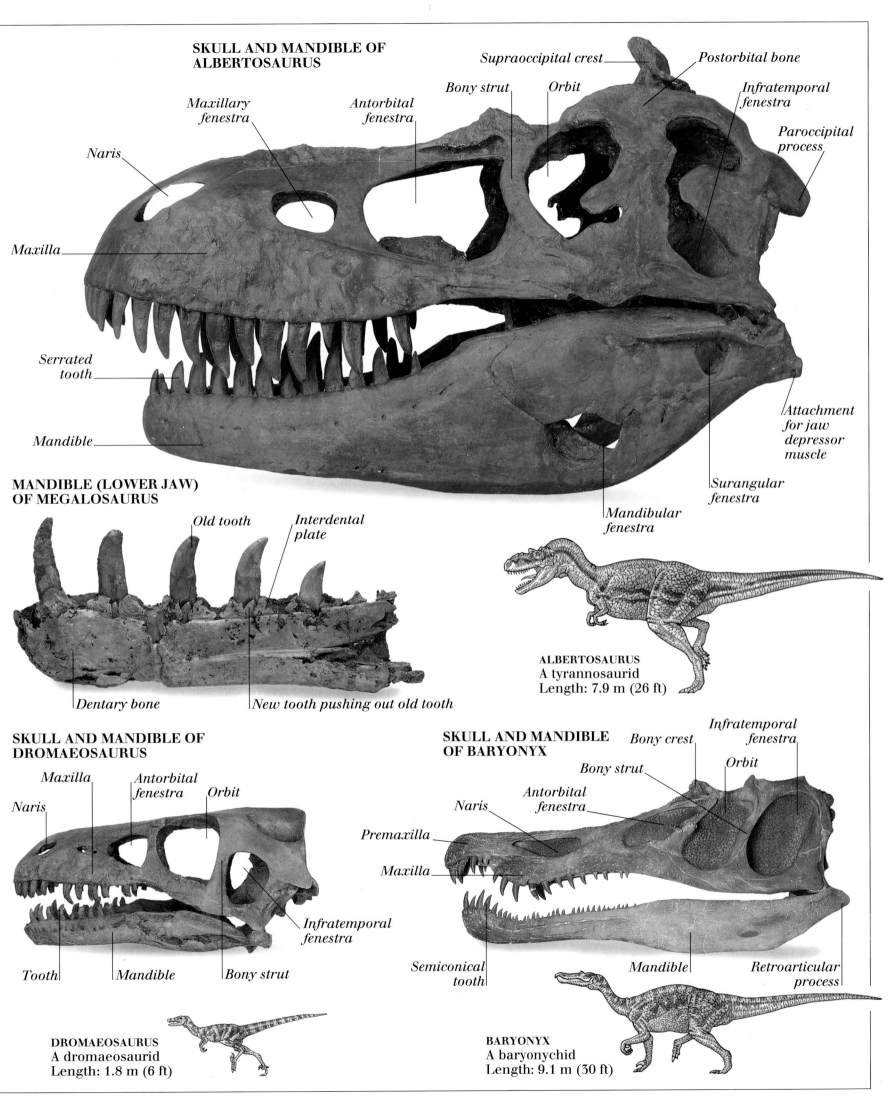

SKULL AND MANDIBLE OF ALBERTOSAURUS

Naris

Maxillary fenestra

Maxilla

Antorbital fenestra

Bony strut

Orbit

Supraoccipital crest

Postorbital bone

Infratemporal fenestra

Paroccipital process

Serrated tooth

Mandible

Attachment for jaw depressor muscle

Surangular fenestra

Mandibular fenestra

MANDIBLE (LOWER JAW) OF MEGALOSAURUS

Old tooth

Interdental plate

Dentary bone

New tooth pushing out old tooth

ALBERTOSAURUS
A tyrannosaurid
Length: 7.9 m (26 ft)

SKULL AND MANDIBLE OF DROMAEOSAURUS

Maxilla

Naris

Antorbital fenestra

Orbit

Infratemporal fenestra

Tooth

Mandible

Bony strut

DROMAEOSAURUS
A dromaeosaurid
Length: 1.8 m (6 ft)

SKULL AND MANDIBLE OF BARYONYX

Bony crest

Infratemporal fenestra

Bony strut

Orbit

Naris

Antorbital fenestra

Premaxilla

Maxilla

Semiconical tooth

Mandible

Retroarticular process

BARYONYX
A baryonychid
Length: 9.1 m (30 ft)

Small ornithopods

SMALL ORNITHOPODS IS A GENERAL TERM for a varied collection
of ornithischian (bird-hipped), herbivorous (plant-eating)
dinosaurs that were widespread from Late Triassic to
Late Cretaceous times (231–65 million years ago). Most of these dinosaurs
were relatively small – typically less than about 4 m (13 ft) long. However, a
few were considerably larger; for example, *Tenontosaurus* was about 6.4 m
(21 ft) long. Large ornithopods, as their name suggests, were generally
bigger than small ornithopods and included iguanodonts (see pp. 36-37)
and hadrosaurs (see pp. 38-41). Most small ornithopods had the typical
ornithischian arrangement of a toothless beak and cheek teeth for grinding up
vegetation. However, the heterodontosaurids (meaning "different-tooth lizards")
had three distinct types of teeth – sharp cutting teeth at the front, two pairs of long,
canine-like teeth, and broad-ridged cheek teeth at the back of the mouth – an
arrangement that is extremely unusual for herbivores of any kind.

(see pp. 36-37)
(see pp. 38-41)

**EXAMPLES OF SMALL
ORNITHOPODS**

ORODROMEUS
A hypsilophodontid
Length: 2.4 m (8 ft)

INTERNAL ANATOMY OF FEMALE HYPSILOPHODON

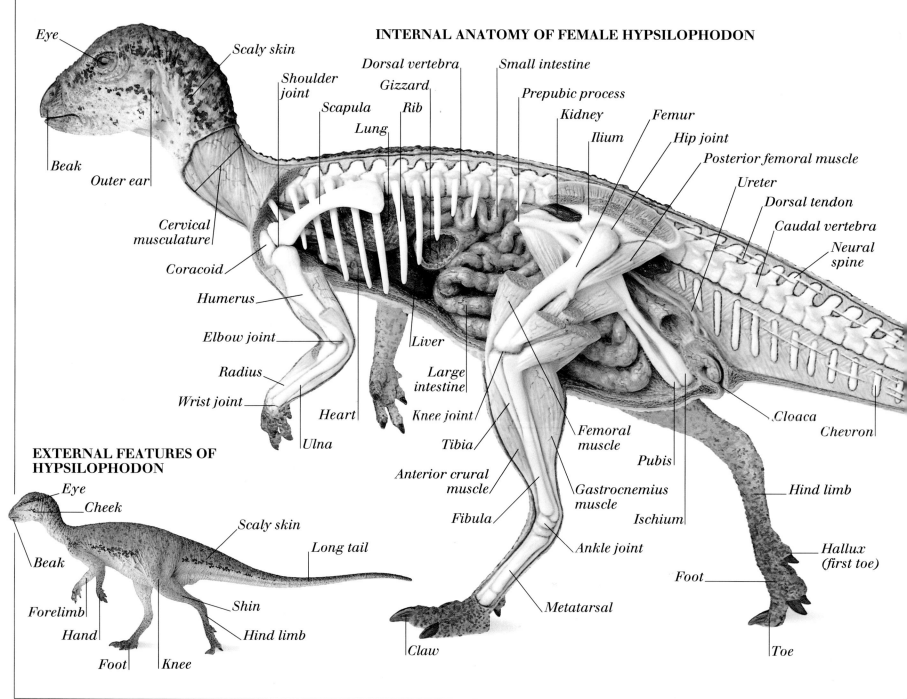

Eye

Scaly skin

Shoulder joint

Dorsal vertebra

Gizzard

Small intestine

Prepubic process

Scapula

Rib

Kidney

Femur

Lung

Ilium

Hip joint

Beak

Posterior femoral muscle

Outer ear

Ureter

Dorsal tendon

Cervical musculature

Caudal vertebra

Neural spine

Coracoid

Humerus

Elbow joint

Liver

Radius

Large intestine

Wrist joint

Heart

Knee joint

Cloaca

Chevron

Ulna

Tibia

Femoral muscle

EXTERNAL FEATURES OF HYPSILOPHODON

Anterior crural muscle

Pubis

Eye

Cheek

Gastrocnemius muscle

Hind limb

Scaly skin

Ischium

Beak

Long tail

Fibula

Ankle joint

Hallux (first toe)

Forelimb

Shin

Metatarsal

Foot

Hand

Hind limb

Claw

Toe

Foot

Knee

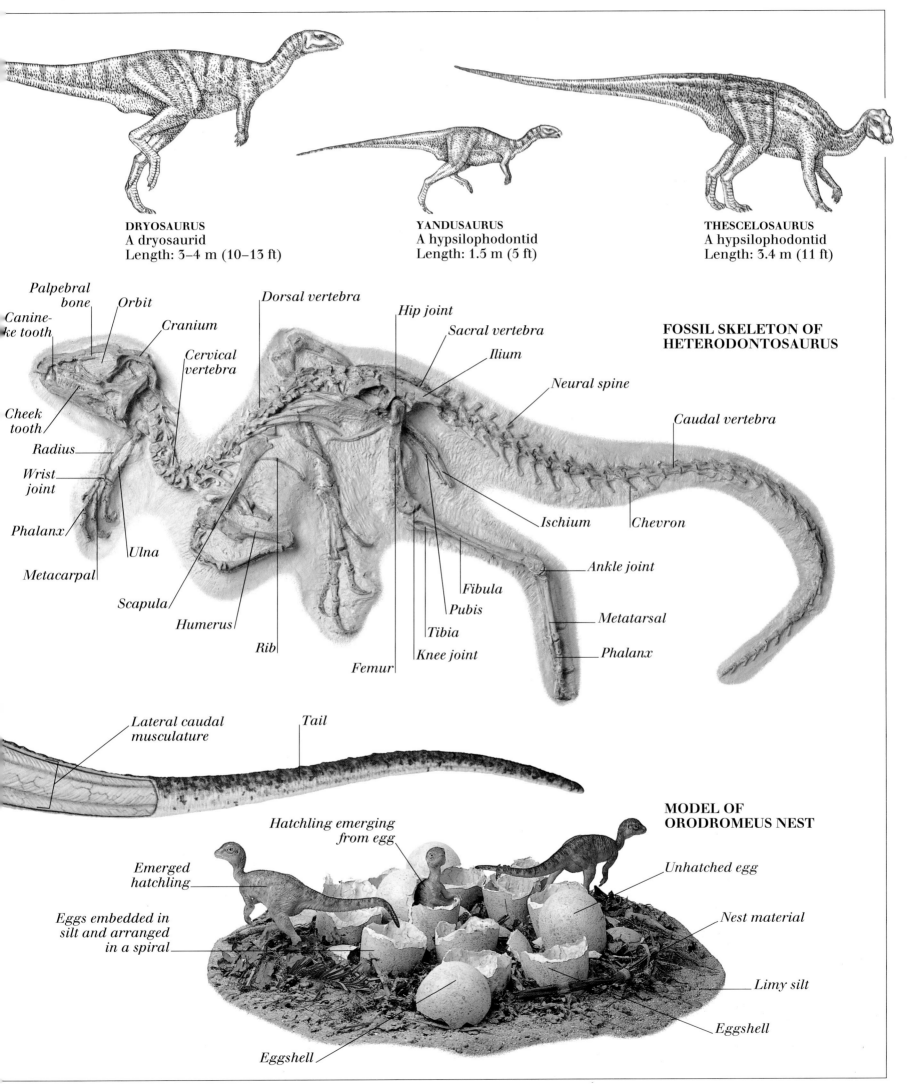

DRYOSAURUS
A dryosaurid
Length: 3–4 m (10–13 ft)

YANDUSAURUS
A hypsilophodontid
Length: 1.5 m (5 ft)

THESCELOSAURUS
A hypsilophodontid
Length: 3.4 m (11 ft)

Palpebral
bone

Orbit

Canine-
ke tooth

Cranium

Dorsal vertebra

Hip joint

Sacral vertebra

**FOSSIL SKELETON OF
HETERODONTOSAURUS**

Cervical
vertebra

Ilium

Neural spine

Cheek
tooth

Caudal vertebra

Radius

Wrist
joint

Phalanx

Ischium

Chevron

Ulna

Ankle joint

Metacarpal

Fibula

Scapula

Pubis

Metatarsal

Humerus

Tibia

Phalanx

Rib

Knee joint

Femur

Lateral caudal
musculature

Tail

**MODEL OF
ORODROMEUS NEST**

Hatchling emerging
from egg

Emerged
hatchling

Unhatched egg

Eggs embedded in
silt and arranged
in a spiral

Nest material

Limy silt

Eggshell

Eggshell

Iguanodonts

IGUANODON TOOTH

IGUANODONTS WERE A GROUP of herbivorous (plant-eating), ornithischian (bird-hipped) dinosaurs that lived from Late Jurassic to Late Cretaceous times (165–70 million years ago). They were medium- to large-sized dinosaurs – between 3.5 m (11 ft 6 in) and 10 m (33 ft) long – and lived in what are now North America, Europe, Africa, Asia, and Australia. Typically, iguanodonts had a broad, toothless beak at the end of a long snout; large jaws with long rows of ridged, close-packed cheek teeth for grinding vegetation; a bulky body; and a heavy tail that was stiffened by bony tendons. Iguanodonts' powerful hind limbs enabled them to run from danger, but hoof-like nails on their fingers and toes indicate that they often walked on all fours. *Iguanodon*, and probably some other iguanodonts, had large thumb-spikes that were strong enough to stab attackers, and flexible little fingers. The most unusual iguanodont was *Ouranosaurus*, which had a "sail" along its back. The sail consisted of skin stretched tightly over upright spines and probably served to regulate body temperature by absorbing and radiating heat. Some authorities believe that all iguanodonts belong to one group, the iguanodontids. However, others divide them into two subgroups: iguanodontids, such as *Iguanodon*, *Ouranosaurus*, and *Probactrosaurus*, and camptosaurids, such as *Camptosaurus* and possibly *Muttaburrasaurus*. This division is based on the number of toes of the dinosaurs: iguanodontids had three toes, whereas camptosaurids had four.

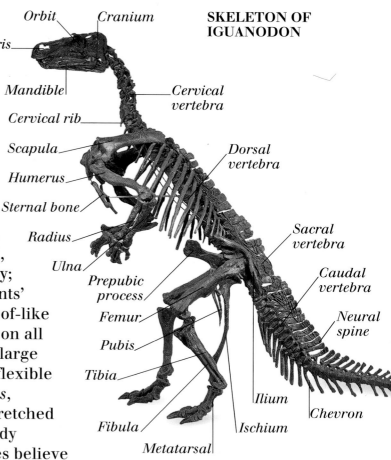

SKELETON OF IGUANODON

Orbit
Cranium
Naris
Mandible
Cervical vertebra
Cervical rib
Scapula
Dorsal vertebra
Humerus
Sternal bone
Radius
Sacral vertebra
Ulna
Prepubic process
Caudal vertebra
Femur
Neural spine
Pubis
Tibia
Ilium
Chevron
Fibula
Ischium
Metatarsal

Thigh

Heavy, stiff tail

Knee

Hind limb

Ankle

Toe

Foot

Hoof-like nail

SKULL AND MANDIBLE OF YOUNG IGUANODON

Maxilla
Cheek tooth
Orbit
Cranium
Premaxilla
Paroccipital process
Jugal bone
Coronoid process
Predentary bone
Dentary bone
Mandible

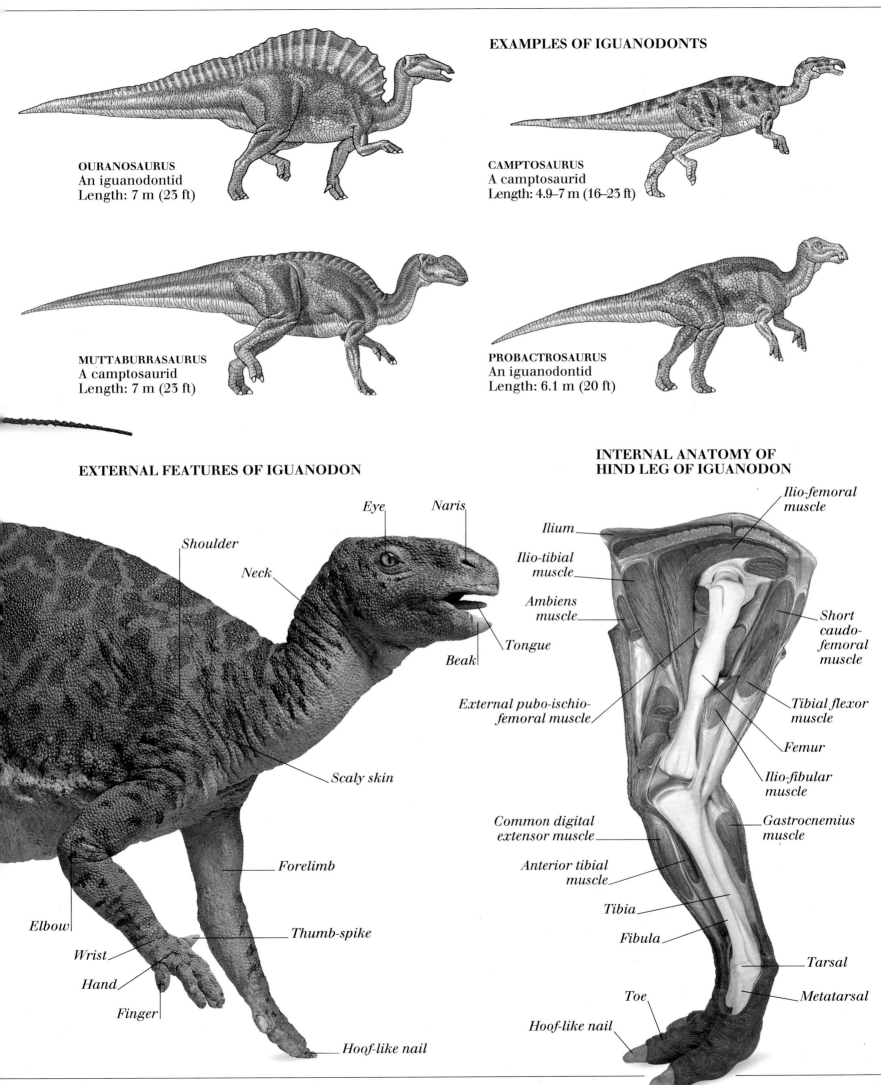

EXAMPLES OF IGUANODONTS

OURANOSAURUS
An iguanodontid
Length: 7 m (23 ft)

CAMPTOSAURUS
A camptosaurid
Length: 4.9–7 m (16–23 ft)

MUTTABURRASAURUS
A camptosaurid
Length: 7 m (23 ft)

PROBACTROSAURUS
An iguanodontid
Length: 6.1 m (20 ft)

EXTERNAL FEATURES OF IGUANODON

Eye

Naris

Shoulder

Neck

Tongue

Beak

Scaly skin

Forelimb

Elbow

Wrist

Hand

Thumb-spike

Finger

Hoof-like nail

INTERNAL ANATOMY OF HIND LEG OF IGUANODON

Ilio-femoral muscle

Ilium

Ilio-tibial muscle

Ambiens muscle

Short caudo-femoral muscle

External pubo-ischio-femoral muscle

Tibial flexor muscle

Femur

Ilio-fibular muscle

Common digital extensor muscle

Gastrocnemius muscle

Anterior tibial muscle

Tibia

Fibula

Tarsal

Toe

Metatarsal

Hoof-like nail

37

Hadrosaurs 1

FOSSIL SKELETON OF
YOUNG HADROSAUR

HADROSAURS WERE a group of ornithischian (bird-hipped) dinosaurs that lived during Late Cretaceous times (97.5–65 million years ago) in what are now North America, Asia, and Europe. A characteristic feature of these herbivorous (plant-eating) dinosaurs was a beak similar to a duck's bill, which is the reason why hadrosaurs are sometimes known as duckbills. Although the beak was toothless, hadrosaurs had large numbers of cheek teeth – sometimes more than 300 in each jaw – for grinding tough vegetation. Hadrosaurs ranged from 4 m (13 ft) to 14.9 m (49 ft) in length. They walked on all fours but ran on their hind limbs, balancing their heavy bodies with a long, stiffened tail. There were two main subgroups of hadrosaurs: hadrosaurines, such as *Gryposaurus* and *Maiasaura*, and lambeosaurines, such as *Corythosaurus* and *Parasaurolophus*. The main difference between the subgroups was the shape of the skull. Hadrosaurines had flat skulls, some with bumps of solid bone on the snout, whereas the skulls of lambeosaurines had large, hollow, bony crests.

Labels (young Maiasaura skeleton): Dorsal vertebrae, Sacral vertebrae, Caudal vertebrae, Cervical vertebrae, Cranium, Orbit, Ilium, Ischium, Pubis, Knee joint, Femur, Mandible, Fibula, Elbow joint, Tibia, Ankle joint, Phalanges, Metatarsals, Wrist joint, Phalanges, Metacarpals

FOSSIL SKELETON OF GRYPOSAURUS

Labels (Gryposaurus): Caudal vertebrae (end vertebrae missing), Neural spine, Chevron, Ossified tendon, Ischium, Ankle joint

MODEL OF MAIASAURA NEST

Labels (nest): Rounded top end of egg, Emerging hatchling, Hatchling, Eggshell fragment, Plant material to protect and warm eggs, Raised nest made of sand, Unhatched egg

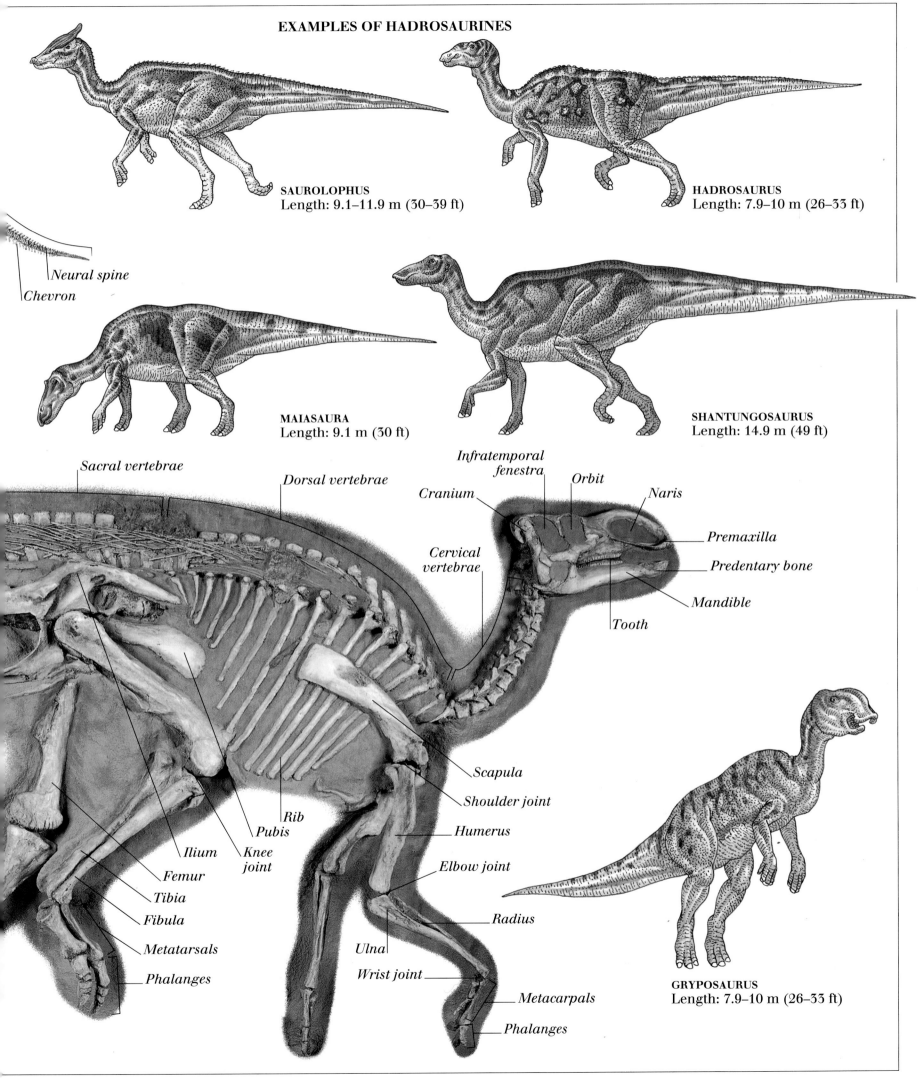

EXAMPLES OF HADROSAURINES

SAUROLOPHUS
Length: 9.1–11.9 m (30–39 ft)

HADROSAURUS
Length: 7.9–10 m (26–33 ft)

Neural spine

Chevron

MAIASAURA
Length: 9.1 m (30 ft)

SHANTUNGOSAURUS
Length: 14.9 m (49 ft)

Sacral vertebrae

Dorsal vertebrae

Infratemporal fenestra

Cranium

Orbit

Naris

Premaxilla

Cervical vertebrae

Predentary bone

Mandible

Tooth

Scapula

Shoulder joint

Humerus

Elbow joint

Rib

Pubis

Ilium

Knee joint

Femur

Tibia

Radius

Fibula

Ulna

Metatarsals

Wrist joint

Phalanges

Metacarpals

Phalanges

GRYPOSAURUS
Length: 7.9–10 m (26–33 ft)

Hadrosaurs 2

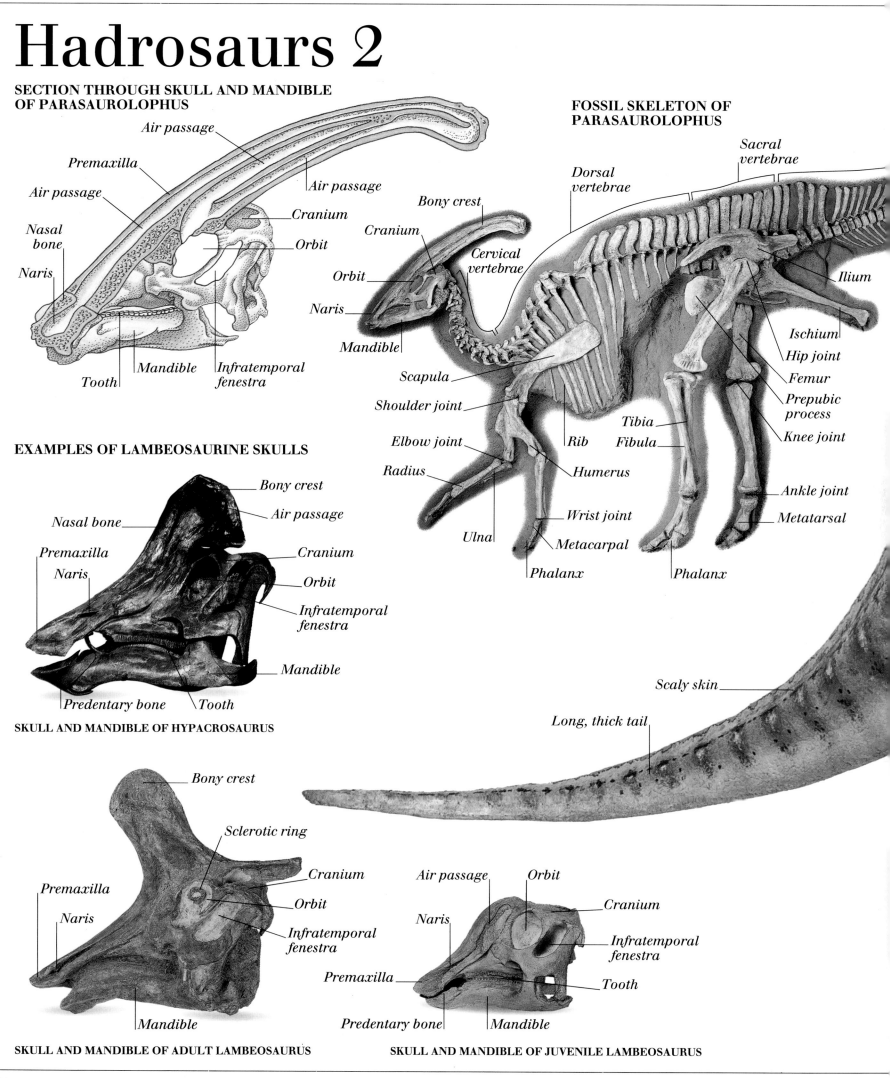

SECTION THROUGH SKULL AND MANDIBLE OF PARASAUROLOPHUS

Air passage

Premaxilla

Air passage

Nasal bone

Naris

Cranium

Air passage

Orbit

Tooth

Mandible

Infratemporal fenestra

FOSSIL SKELETON OF PARASAUROLOPHUS

Sacral vertebrae

Dorsal vertebrae

Bony crest

Cranium

Cervical vertebrae

Orbit

Naris

Mandible

Scapula

Shoulder joint

Elbow joint

Radius

Ulna

Phalanx

Wrist joint

Metacarpal

Rib

Humerus

Tibia

Fibula

Ilium

Ischium

Hip joint

Femur

Prepubic process

Knee joint

Ankle joint

Metatarsal

Phalanx

Scaly skin

Long, thick tail

EXAMPLES OF LAMBEOSAURINE SKULLS

Bony crest

Air passage

Nasal bone

Premaxilla

Naris

Cranium

Orbit

Infratemporal fenestra

Mandible

Predentary bone

Tooth

SKULL AND MANDIBLE OF HYPACROSAURUS

Bony crest

Sclerotic ring

Cranium

Orbit

Premaxilla

Naris

Infratemporal fenestra

Mandible

SKULL AND MANDIBLE OF ADULT LAMBEOSAURUS

Air passage

Orbit

Naris

Cranium

Premaxilla

Infratemporal fenestra

Tooth

Predentary bone

Mandible

SKULL AND MANDIBLE OF JUVENILE LAMBEOSAURUS

EXTERNAL FEATURES OF CORYTHOSAURUS

Bony crest

Eye

Naris

Toothless beak

Tongue

Cheek pouch

Caudal vertebrae

Neural spine

Chevron

Neck

Shoulder

Forelimb

Elbow

Wrist

Hand

Finger

Nail

Knee

Thigh

Tubercle

Hind limb

Ankle

Foot

Toe

Nail

EXAMPLES OF LAMBEOSAURINES

CORYTHOSAURUS
Length: 10 m (33 ft)

PARASAUROLOPHUS
Length: 10 m (33 ft)

HYPACROSAURUS
Length: 9.1 m (30 ft)

LAMBEOSAURUS
Length: 14.9 m (49 ft)

Stegosaurs

STEGOSAURS WERE A GROUP of ornithischian (bird-hipped) dinosaurs that lived from Middle Jurassic to Late Cretaceous times (188–65 million years ago) in what are now North America, Europe, Africa, and Asia. They were medium-sized dinosaurs – between about 3 m (10 ft) and 9.1 m (30 ft) long – with bulky bodies that weighed up to about 1.5 tonnes (1.47 tons). The main characteristic of stegosaurs was the two rows of dorsal plates or spines that ran along their backs. The exact function of these plates or spikes is not known, but it is thought that they may have been for defence, for display, or for regulating body temperature by absorbing or radiating heat. Also for defence, stegosaurs had caudal (tail) spikes and, in some species, shoulder spikes. There were two main subgroups of stegosaurs: stegosaurids, such as *Stegosaurus*, *Tuojiangosaurus*, *Kentrosaurus*, and *Wuerhosaurus*, and huayangosaurids. *Huayangosaurus*, the only known huayangosaurid, resembled stegosaurids but is thought to have been more primitive.

EXAMPLES OF STEGOSAURS

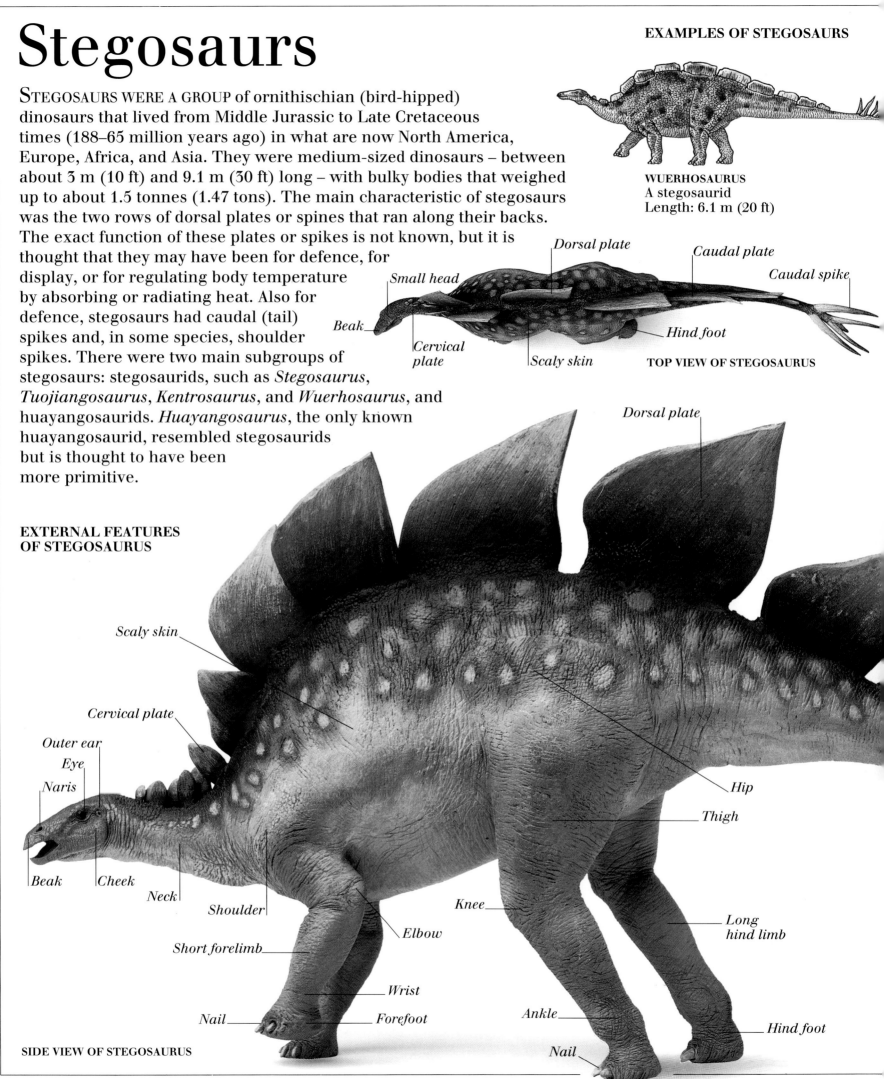

WUERHOSAURUS
A stegosaurid
Length: 6.1 m (20 ft)

Dorsal plate

Caudal plate

Caudal spike

Small head

Beak

Cervical plate

Hind foot

Scaly skin

TOP VIEW OF STEGOSAURUS

Dorsal plate

**EXTERNAL FEATURES
OF STEGOSAURUS**

Scaly skin

Cervical plate

Outer ear

Eye

Naris

Hip

Thigh

Beak

Cheek

Neck

Shoulder

Knee

Long
hind limb

Elbow

Short forelimb

Wrist

Nail

Forefoot

Ankle

Hind foot

Nail

SIDE VIEW OF STEGOSAURUS

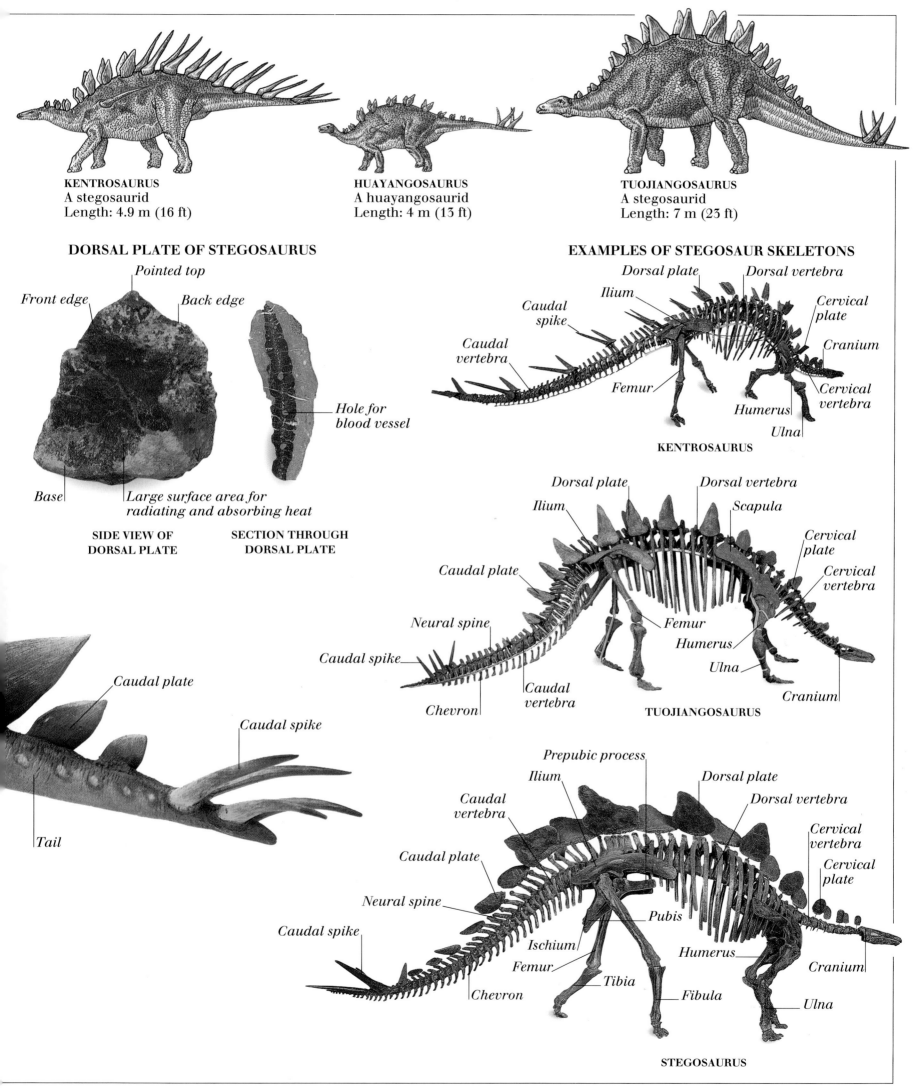

KENTROSAURUS
A stegosaurid
Length: 4.9 m (16 ft)

HUAYANGOSAURUS
A huayangosaurid
Length: 4 m (13 ft)

TUOJIANGOSAURUS
A stegosaurid
Length: 7 m (23 ft)

DORSAL PLATE OF STEGOSAURUS

Pointed top

Front edge

Back edge

Hole for
blood vessel

Base

Large surface area for
radiating and absorbing heat

**SIDE VIEW OF
DORSAL PLATE**

**SECTION THROUGH
DORSAL PLATE**

Caudal plate

Caudal spike

Tail

EXAMPLES OF STEGOSAUR SKELETONS

Dorsal plate

Dorsal vertebra

Ilium

Cervical
plate

Caudal
spike

Cranium

Caudal
vertebra

Cervical
vertebra

Femur

Humerus

Ulna

KENTROSAURUS

Dorsal plate

Dorsal vertebra

Ilium

Scapula

Caudal plate

Cervical
plate

Cervical
vertebra

Neural spine

Femur

Humerus

Caudal spike

Ulna

Caudal
vertebra

Cranium

Chevron

TUOJIANGOSAURUS

Prepubic process

Ilium

Dorsal plate

Caudal
vertebra

Dorsal vertebra

Cervical
vertebra

Caudal plate

Cervical
plate

Neural spine

Pubis

Caudal spike

Ischium

Humerus

Femur

Cranium

Tibia

Fibula

Chevron

Ulna

STEGOSAURUS

Ankylosaurs

ANKYLOSAURS WERE A GROUP OF HERBIVOROUS (plant-eating), ornithischian (bird-hipped) dinosaurs that lived from Middle Jurassic to Late Cretaceous times (188–65 million years ago) in what are now Mongolia, North America, Antarctica, Australia, and Europe. They ranged from 2.4 m (8 ft) to 10.7 m (35 ft) long, and weighed up to 2 tonnes (1.9 tons). The most notable feature of these dinosaurs was their heavy armour, which consisted of bony studs, plates, and spikes that protected them from predators. Ankylosaurs also had characteristics typical of herbivorous dinosaurs: toothless beaks and cheek teeth for cropping and chewing vegetation. It is probable that ankylosaurs also had a gizzard (muscular stomach) and gastroliths (stones) for further breaking down plant material in the gut. There were two main subgroups of ankylosaurs: ankylosaurids, such as *Ankylosaurus*, *Euoplocephalus*, and *Pinacosaurus*; and nodosaurids, such as *Edmontonia*, *Minmi*, *Panoplosaurus*, and *Polacanthus*. The most apparent differences between the subgroups were that ankylosaurids had horns on their head and a bony tail-club, whereas nodosaurids tended to have neither.

SHOULDER
SPIKE OF
POLACANTHUS

**EXAMPLES OF
ANKYLOSAURS**

MINMI
A nodosaurid
Length: 2.4 m (8 ft)

**FOSSIL OF ANKYLOSAURUS
TAIL CLUB**

Ossified caudal
vertebra

Lateral plate

Terminal
plate

**INTERNAL ANATOMY OF
FEMALE EUOPLOCEPHALUS**

Shoulder spike

Scapula

Shoulder joint

Cervical
musculature

Head
horn

Toothless
beak

Wrist joint

Metacarpal

Coracoid

Humerus

Radius

Ventral
antebrachial
muscle

Ulna

Elbow joint

Heart

Liver

Large
intestine

Lung

Rib

Dorsal
vertebra

Small
intestine

Gizzard

Ilio-tibial muscle

Ilium

Ischium

Reproductive duct

Caudal vertebra

Neural spine

Ureter

Ilio-
tibial
muscle

Fibula

Digital
extensor
muscle

Femur

Knee joint

Gastrocnemius
muscle

Ankle joint

Metatarsal

Chevron

Cloaca

44

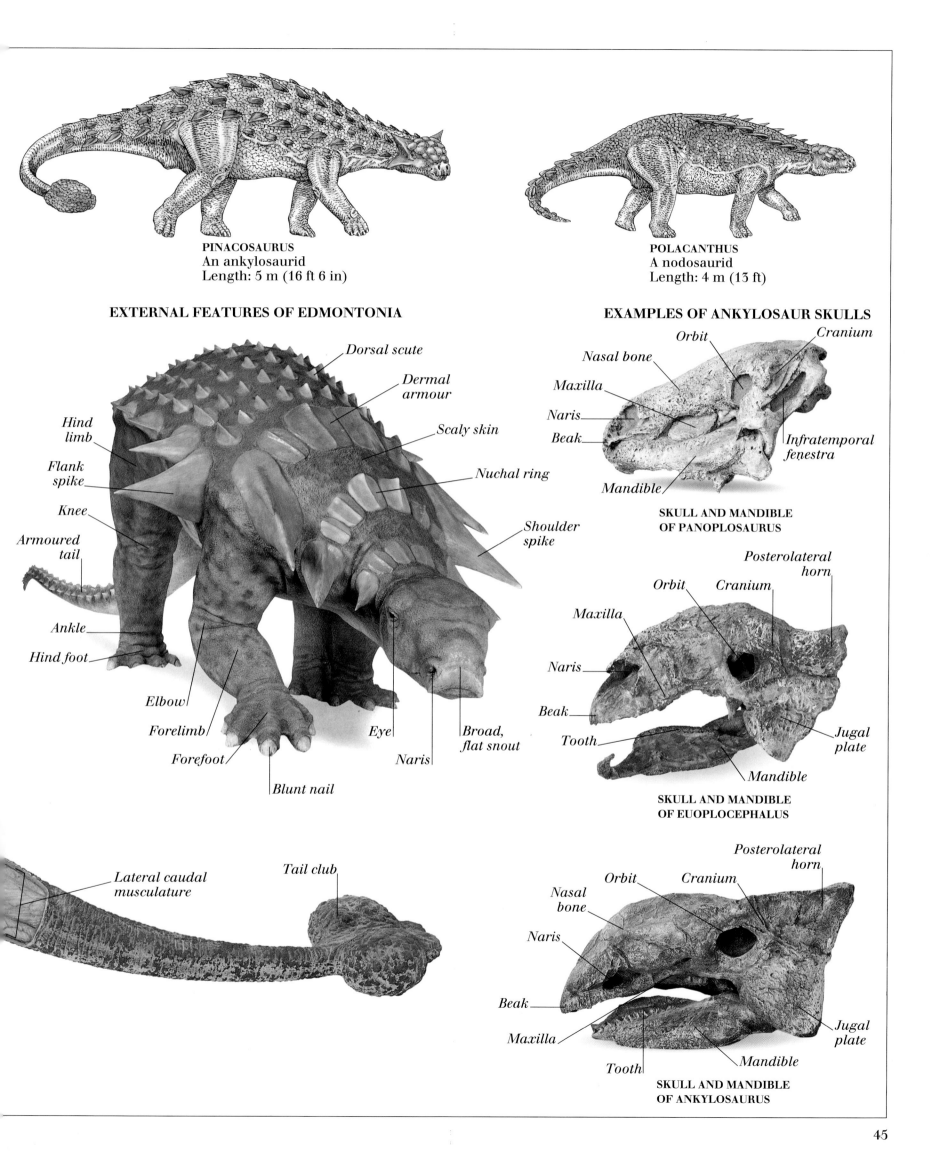

PINACOSAURUS
An ankylosaurid
Length: 5 m (16 ft 6 in)

POLACANTHUS
A nodosaurid
Length: 4 m (13 ft)

EXTERNAL FEATURES OF EDMONTONIA

Dorsal scute

Dermal armour

Scaly skin

Nuchal ring

Shoulder spike

Hind limb

Flank spike

Knee

Armoured tail

Ankle

Hind foot

Elbow

Forelimb

Forefoot

Blunt nail

Eye

Naris

Broad, flat snout

EXAMPLES OF ANKYLOSAUR SKULLS

Orbit

Cranium

Nasal bone

Maxilla

Naris

Beak

Infratemporal fenestra

Mandible

SKULL AND MANDIBLE OF PANOPLOSAURUS

Posterolateral horn

Orbit

Cranium

Maxilla

Naris

Beak

Tooth

Jugal plate

Mandible

SKULL AND MANDIBLE OF EUOPLOCEPHALUS

Lateral caudal musculature

Tail club

Posterolateral horn

Orbit

Cranium

Nasal bone

Naris

Beak

Maxilla

Tooth

Mandible

Jugal plate

SKULL AND MANDIBLE OF ANKYLOSAURUS

Pachycephalosaurs

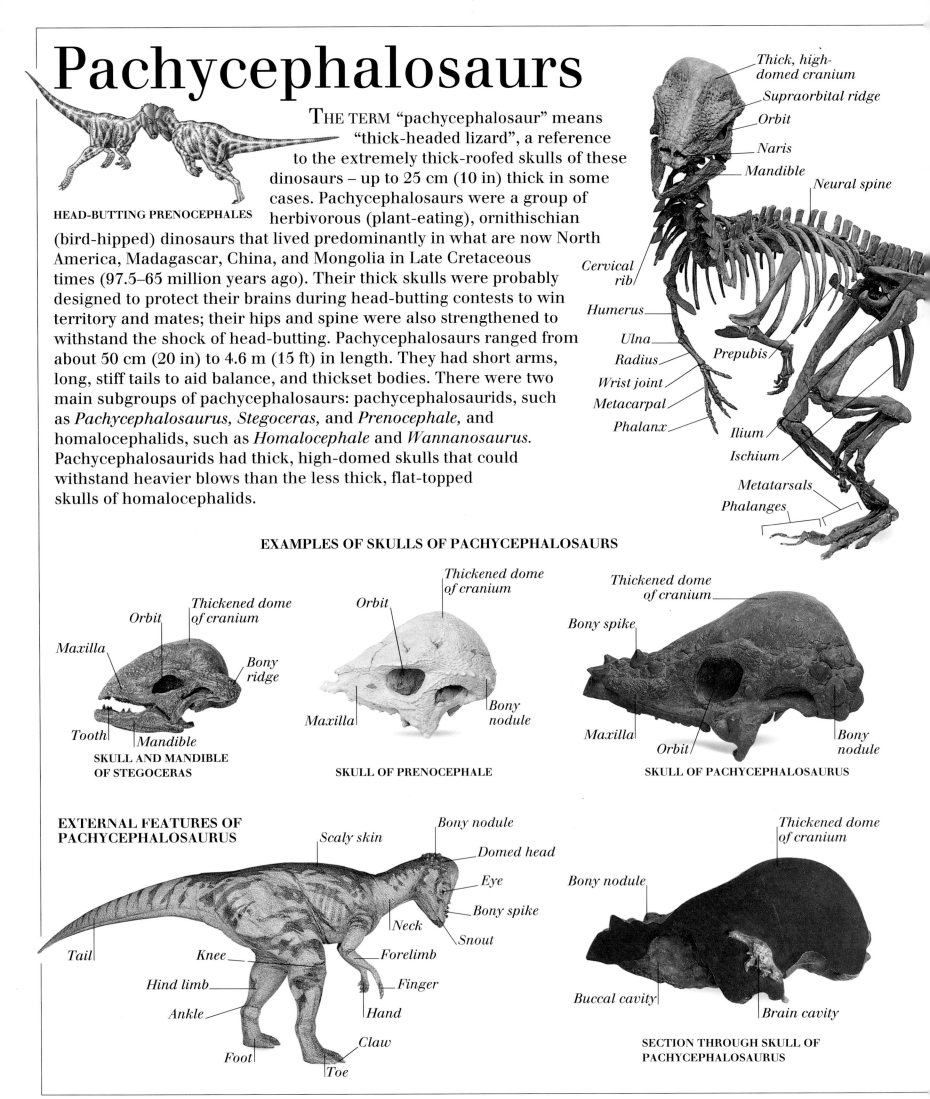

THE TERM "pachycephalosaur" means "thick-headed lizard", a reference to the extremely thick-roofed skulls of these dinosaurs – up to 25 cm (10 in) thick in some cases. Pachycephalosaurs were a group of herbivorous (plant-eating), ornithischian (bird-hipped) dinosaurs that lived predominantly in what are now North America, Madagascar, China, and Mongolia in Late Cretaceous times (97.5–65 million years ago). Their thick skulls were probably designed to protect their brains during head-butting contests to win territory and mates; their hips and spine were also strengthened to withstand the shock of head-butting. Pachycephalosaurs ranged from about 50 cm (20 in) to 4.6 m (15 ft) in length. They had short arms, long, stiff tails to aid balance, and thickset bodies. There were two main subgroups of pachycephalosaurs: pachycephalosaurids, such as *Pachycephalosaurus*, *Stegoceras*, and *Prenocephale*, and homalocephalids, such as *Homalocephale* and *Wannanosaurus*. Pachycephalosaurids had thick, high-domed skulls that could withstand heavier blows than the less thick, flat-topped skulls of homalocephalids.

HEAD-BUTTING PRENOCEPHALES

Thick, high-domed cranium
Supraorbital ridge
Orbit
Naris
Mandible
Neural spine
Cervical rib
Humerus
Ulna
Radius
Prepubis
Wrist joint
Metacarpal
Phalanx
Ilium
Ischium
Metatarsals
Phalanges

EXAMPLES OF SKULLS OF PACHYCEPHALOSAURS

Orbit
Thickened dome of cranium
Maxilla
Bony ridge
Tooth
Mandible

SKULL AND MANDIBLE OF STEGOCERAS

Thickened dome of cranium
Orbit
Maxilla
Bony nodule

SKULL OF PRENOCEPHALE

Thickened dome of cranium
Bony spike
Maxilla
Orbit
Bony nodule

SKULL OF PACHYCEPHALOSAURUS

EXTERNAL FEATURES OF PACHYCEPHALOSAURUS

Scaly skin
Bony nodule
Domed head
Eye
Bony spike
Neck
Snout
Forelimb
Finger
Hand
Knee
Tail
Hind limb
Ankle
Claw
Foot
Toe

Thickened dome of cranium
Bony nodule
Buccal cavity
Brain cavity

SECTION THROUGH SKULL OF PACHYCEPHALOSAURUS

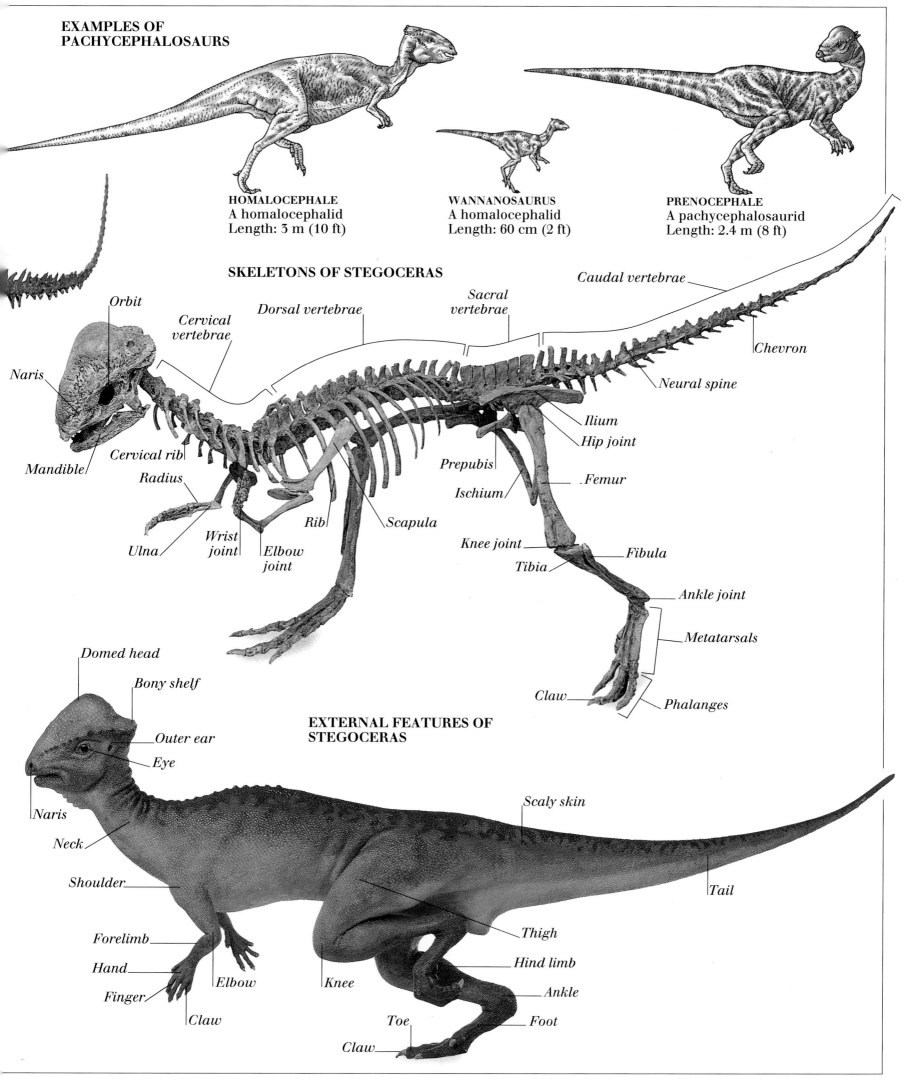

**EXAMPLES OF
PACHYCEPHALOSAURS**

HOMALOCEPHALE
A homalocephalid
Length: 3 m (10 ft)

WANNANOSAURUS
A homalocephalid
Length: 60 cm (2 ft)

PRENOCEPHALE
A pachycephalosaurid
Length: 2.4 m (8 ft)

SKELETONS OF STEGOCERAS

Orbit

*Cervical
vertebrae*

Dorsal vertebrae

*Sacral
vertebrae*

Caudal vertebrae

Naris

Chevron

Neural spine

Ilium

Hip joint

Cervical rib

Prepubis

Mandible

Femur

Radius

Ischium

Rib

Scapula

Knee joint

Fibula

*Wrist
joint*

*Elbow
joint*

Tibia

Ulna

Ankle joint

Metatarsals

Claw

Phalanges

Domed head

Bony shelf

**EXTERNAL FEATURES OF
STEGOCERAS**

Outer ear

Eye

Scaly skin

Naris

Neck

Tail

Shoulder

Thigh

Forelimb

Hind limb

Hand

Elbow

Knee

Ankle

Finger

Toe

Foot

Claw

Claw

Ceratopsians 1

CERATOPSIANS WERE A GROUP of ornithischian (bird-hipped), herbivorous (plant-eating) dinosaurs with short, deep, parrot-like beaks. These dinosaurs flourished during the Cretaceous period (144–65 million years ago). There were three subgroups of ceratopsians: protoceratopsids, ceratopsids, and psittacosaurids. Protoceratopsids, such as *Protoceratops*, *Bagaceratops*, and *Microceratops*, were relatively small, ranging from 76 cm (30 in) to 3 m (10 ft) long. They had a bony frill around the neck that may have been used to frighten predators, protect the neck, or attract mates; the frill may also have served as an anchor for the jaw muscles. Some species of protoceratopsid also had brow ridges and small horns on their noses and cheeks. Ceratopsids, such as *Triceratops*, *Torosaurus*, *Styracosaurus*, *Pachyrhinosaurus*, and *Eucentrosaurus*, were larger than protoceratopsids, ranging from 1.8 m (6 ft) to 9.1 m (30 ft) in length. *Triceratops*, one of the largest ceratopsids, had a massive head and bulky body, and weighed up to about 5.4 tonnes (5.3 tons). Ceratopsids had neck frills that were larger than those of protoceratopsids, and horns on their brow and nose. In some cases, ceratopsid brow horns were up to 90 cm (3 ft) long. *Psittacosaurus*, the only psittacosaurid known, was 2 m (6 ft 6 in) long. In addition to the parrot-like ceratopsian beak, it had small cheek horns; however, it did not have a bony neck frill.

NEST AND EGGS OF PROTOCERATOPS

SECTION THROUGH CERATOPSIAN EGG

- Yolk sac
- Embryo
- Amniotic sac
- Allantois
- Chorion
- Shell

SKULL AND MANDIBLE OF PROTOCERATOPS

- Parietosquamosal frill
- Cranium
- Postorbital bone
- Orbit
- Nasal bone
- Lacrimal bone
- Naris
- Beak
- Rostral bone
- Parietal fenestra
- Infratemporal fenestra
- Jugal bone
- Surangular bone
- Angular bone
- Predentary bone
- Mandible
- Dentary bone
- Tooth
- Tail

FOSSIL SKELETON OF PROTOCERATOPS

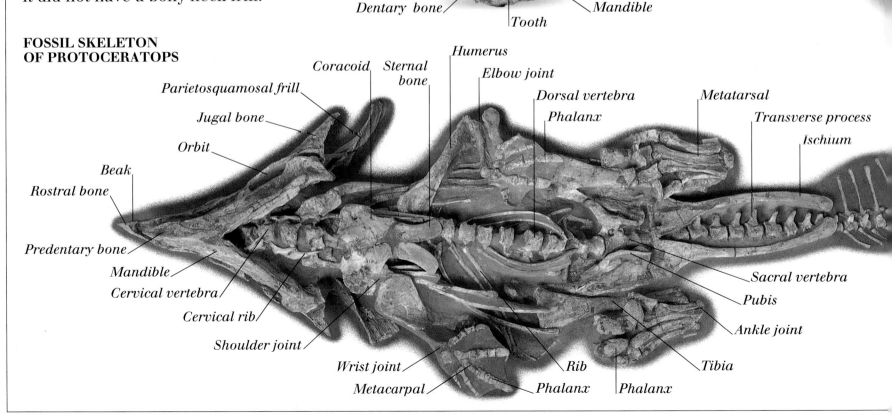

- Coracoid
- Sternal bone
- Humerus
- Elbow joint
- Parietosquamosal frill
- Jugal bone
- Orbit
- Beak
- Rostral bone
- Predentary bone
- Mandible
- Cervical vertebra
- Cervical rib
- Shoulder joint
- Wrist joint
- Metacarpal
- Dorsal vertebra
- Phalanx
- Metatarsal
- Transverse process
- Ischium
- Sacral vertebra
- Pubis
- Ankle joint
- Rib
- Tibia
- Phalanx
- Phalanx

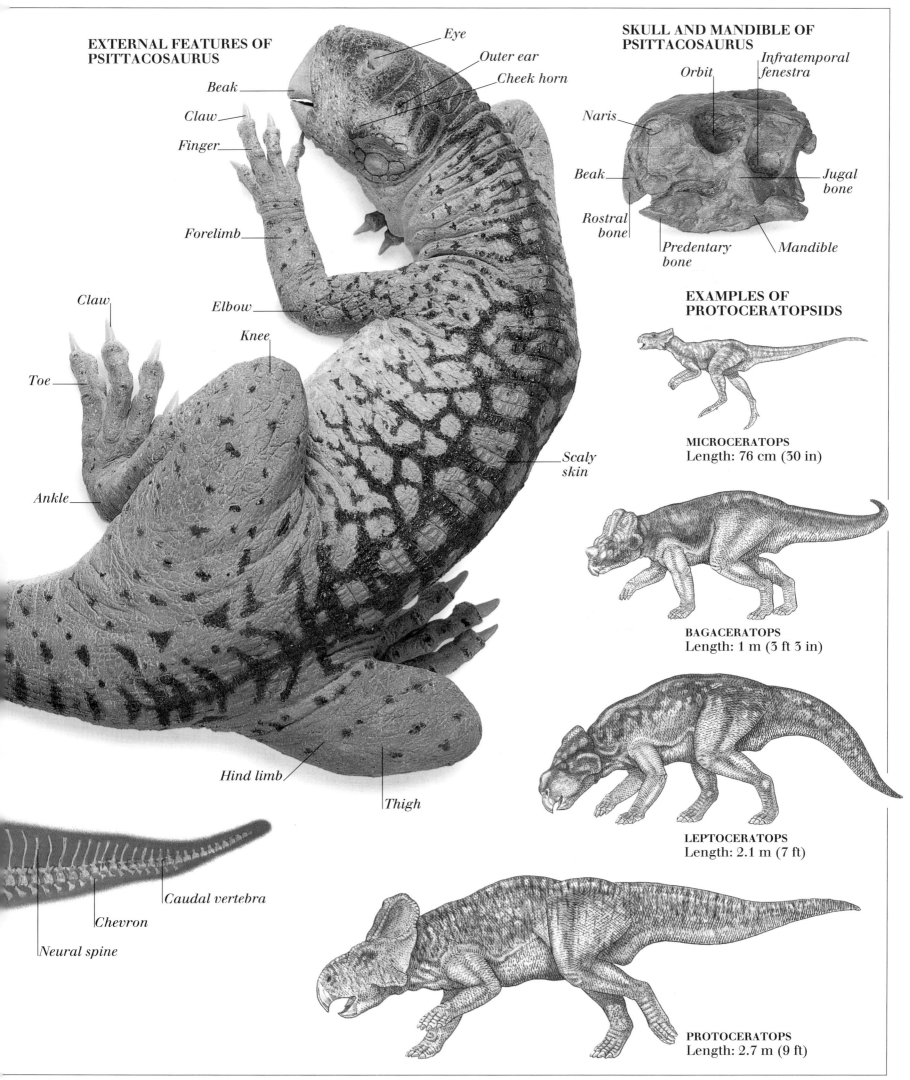

EXTERNAL FEATURES OF PSITTACOSAURUS

Eye

Outer ear

Cheek horn

Beak

Claw

Finger

Forelimb

Elbow

Knee

Claw

Toe

Ankle

Scaly skin

Hind limb

Thigh

Caudal vertebra

Chevron

Neural spine

SKULL AND MANDIBLE OF PSITTACOSAURUS

Orbit

Infratemporal fenestra

Naris

Beak

Jugal bone

Rostral bone

Predentary bone

Mandible

EXAMPLES OF PROTOCERATOPSIDS

MICROCERATOPS
Length: 76 cm (30 in)

BAGACERATOPS
Length: 1 m (3 ft 3 in)

LEPTOCERATOPS
Length: 2.1 m (7 ft)

PROTOCERATOPS
Length: 2.7 m (9 ft)

Ceratopsians 2

EXAMPLES OF CERATOPSIAN SKULLS

Cranium

Brow horn core

Orbit

Parietosquamosal frill

Epoccipital bone

Nose horn core

Naris

Mandible

SKULL AND MANDIBLE OF TRICERATOPS

Parietal fenestra

Nose horn core

Epoccipital bone

Parietosquamosal frill

Supraorbital ridge

Orbit

Naris

Cranium

Mandible

SKULL AND MANDIBLE OF STYRACOSAURUS

Epoccipital bone

Parietal fenestra

Parietosquamosal frill

Brow horn core

Nose horn core

Naris

SKULL OF CHASMOSAURUS

EXTERNAL FEATURES OF TRICERATOPS

Thick, scaly skin

Epoccipital bone

Parietosquamosal frill

Brow horn

Thigh

Nose horn

Tail

Ankle

Knee

Hind limb

Nail

Elbow

Forelimb

Wrist

Eye

Naris

Tongue

Toothless beak

Parietosquamosal frill

Anterior horn core

Supraorbital ridge

Cranium

Orbit

Nose horn core

Parietal fenestra

Naris

Epoccipital bone

Rostral bone

Infratemporal fenestra

Jugal bone

SKULL OF EUCENTROSAURUS

Horn core

Parietal fenestra

Cranium

Nasofrontal boss

Orbit

Epoccipital bone

Naris

Parietosquamosal frill

Rostral bone

Infratemporal fenestra

Jugal bone

SKULL OF PACHYRHINOSAURUS

Ilium

Hip joint

Caudal vertebrae

Ischium

Prepubis

Femur

Knee joint

Fibula

Tibia

Ankle joint

Metatarsals

Phalanges

Chevron

Neural spine

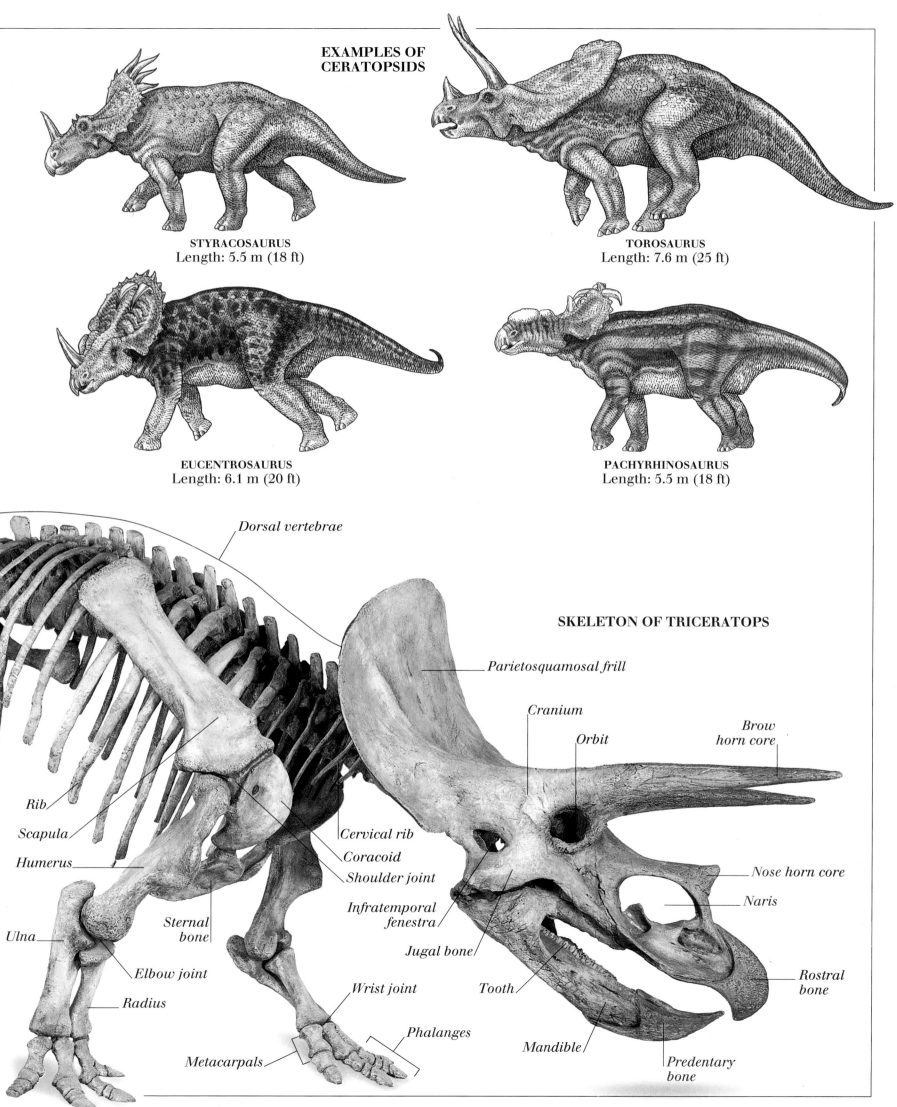

EXAMPLES OF CERATOPSIDS

STYRACOSAURUS
Length: 5.5 m (18 ft)

TOROSAURUS
Length: 7.6 m (25 ft)

EUCENTROSAURUS
Length: 6.1 m (20 ft)

PACHYRHINOSAURUS
Length: 5.5 m (18 ft)

SKELETON OF TRICERATOPS

Dorsal vertebrae

Parietosquamosal frill

Cranium

Orbit

Brow horn core

Rib

Scapula

Cervical rib

Humerus

Coracoid

Shoulder joint

Nose horn core

Infratemporal fenestra

Naris

Ulna

Sternal bone

Jugal bone

Elbow joint

Tooth

Rostral bone

Radius

Wrist joint

Phalanges

Metacarpals

Mandible

Predentary bone

Hands and claws

THE HANDS OF CARNIVOROUS (flesh-eating) dinosaurs – *Deinocheirus* and *Baryonyx*, for example – typically had three fingers (although a few had two), each tipped with a sharp claw. Many carnivorous dinosaurs also had opposable fingers that enabled them to grasp. They walked on their hind legs, leaving their arms and hands free to attack prey. However, the arms of some carnivores, notably *Tyrannosaurus*, were so short that they did not even reach their mouths. Most herbivores (plant-eaters) had padded hands with four or five fingers, tipped with claws or blunt nails. Many herbivores also had sharp thumb-claws for digging or defence. Unlike carnivores, herbivores did not generally have opposable fingers. Although many herbivores – *Iguanodon* and *Prosaurolophus*, for example – had strong, weight-bearing forelimbs, such dinosaurs could also walk or run on their hind legs alone.

FOSSIL OF DINOSAUR CLAW

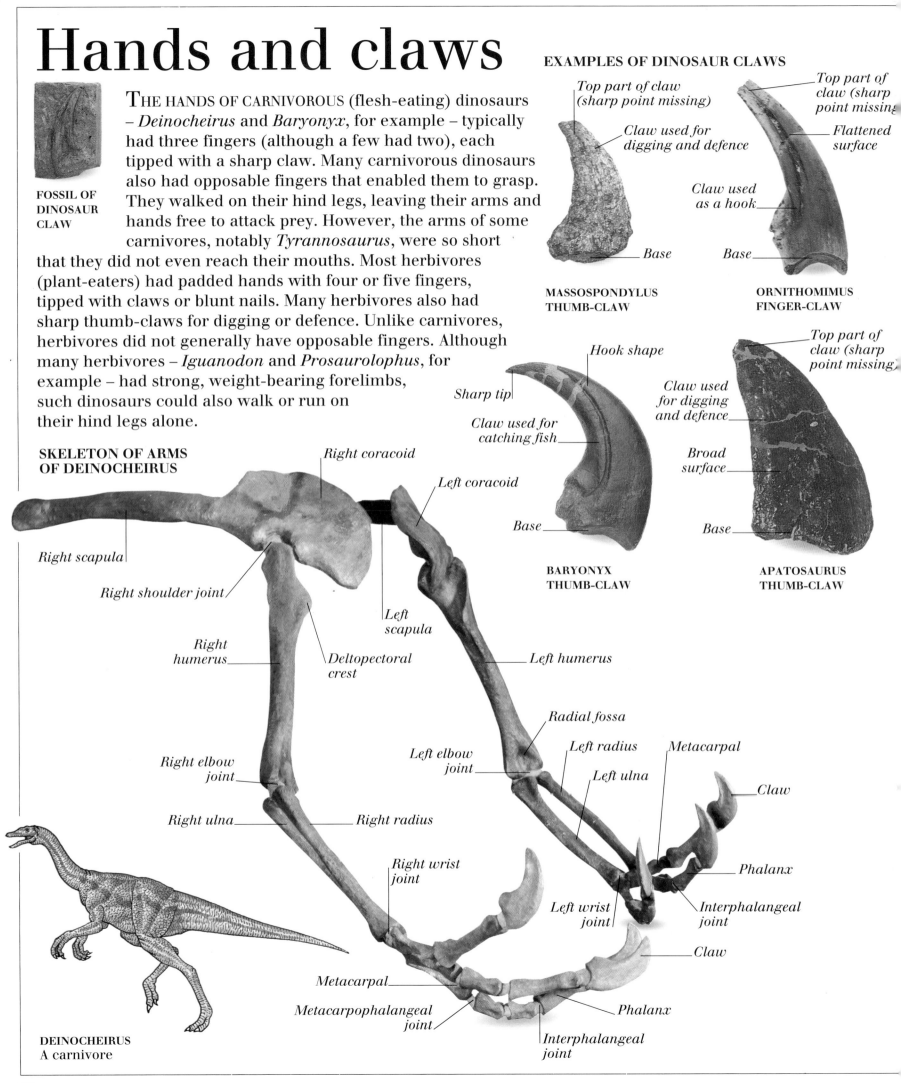

EXAMPLES OF DINOSAUR CLAWS

Top part of claw (sharp point missing)

Claw used for digging and defence

Base

MASSOSPONDYLUS THUMB-CLAW

Top part of claw (sharp point missing)

Flattened surface

Claw used as a hook

Base

ORNITHOMIMUS FINGER-CLAW

Hook shape

Sharp tip

Claw used for catching fish

Base

BARYONYX THUMB-CLAW

Top part of claw (sharp point missing)

Claw used for digging and defence

Broad surface

Base

APATOSAURUS THUMB-CLAW

SKELETON OF ARMS OF DEINOCHEIRUS

Right coracoid

Left coracoid

Right scapula

Right shoulder joint

Left scapula

Right humerus

Deltopectoral crest

Left humerus

Radial fossa

Left elbow joint

Left radius

Metacarpal

Claw

Right elbow joint

Left ulna

Right ulna

Right radius

Phalanx

Right wrist joint

Left wrist joint

Interphalangeal joint

Claw

Metacarpal

Metacarpophalangeal joint

Phalanx

Interphalangeal joint

DEINOCHEIRUS
A carnivore

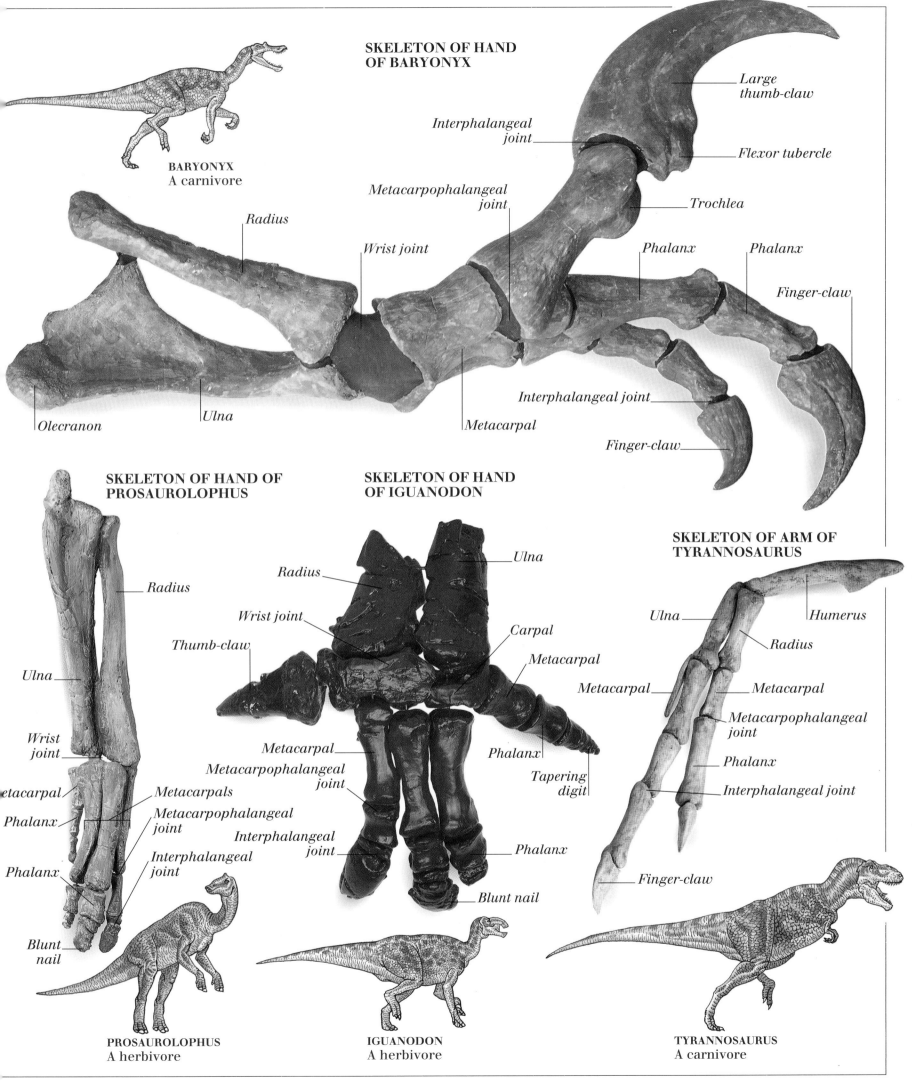

SKELETON OF HAND OF BARYONYX

BARYONYX
A carnivore

Large thumb-claw

Interphalangeal joint

Flexor tubercle

Metacarpophalangeal joint

Trochlea

Wrist joint

Phalanx

Phalanx

Finger-claw

Radius

Interphalangeal joint

Olecranon

Ulna

Metacarpal

Finger-claw

SKELETON OF HAND OF PROSAUROLOPHUS

SKELETON OF HAND OF IGUANODON

SKELETON OF ARM OF TYRANNOSAURUS

Radius

Ulna

Radius

Ulna

Humerus

Wrist joint

Carpal

Radius

Thumb-claw

Metacarpal

Metacarpal

Metacarpal

Ulna

Phalanx

Metacarpophalangeal joint

Wrist joint

Metacarpal

Metacarpophalangeal joint

Tapering digit

Phalanx

etacarpal

Phalanx

Metacarpals

Metacarpophalangeal joint

Interphalangeal joint

Interphalangeal joint

Phalanx

Phalanx

Interphalangeal joint

Blunt nail

Finger-claw

Blunt nail

PROSAUROLOPHUS
A herbivore

IGUANODON
A herbivore

TYRANNOSAURUS
A carnivore

Feet and tracks

DINOSAURS HAD HIGH ankles and walked on their toes. However, apart from these common characteristics, the feet of dinosaurs were extremely diverse. For example, *Stegosaurus*, a large, heavy dinosaur that walked on all fours (a quadruped), had broad, short, elephant-like feet. In contrast, certain large, heavy, semi-quadrupeds (quadrupedal dinosaurs that sometimes walked or ran on their hind legs), such as *Parasaurolophus* and *Iguanodon*, had longer feet with separate toes. Smaller, lighter dinosaurs that walked on two legs (bipeds), such as *Chirostenotes*, *Compsognathus*, and *Dromiceiomimus*, had relatively long, narrow, bird-like feet. The fossilized tracks of some dinosaurs indicate not only the structure of their feet, but also how they moved. For example, the tracks of *Ornithomimus* confirm that it was bipedal, and also indicate that it was lightweight and could run quickly.

**SKELETON OF FOOT
OF PLATEOSAURUS**

*Imprint of foot
of Ornithomimus*

*Imprint
of toe*

*Imprint
of toe*

Material of cast

**FOOT OF
STEGOSAURUS**

Thigh

*Thick,
rough skin*

Knee

Shin

Ankle

Nail

*Elephant-like
foot*

**FOOT OF
COMPSOGNATHUS**

Scaly skin

Shin

Ankle

*Hallux
(first toe)*

Toe

Sharp claw

**CAST OF FOSSILIZED
IGUANODON TRACK**

*Imprint of
hind foot of
Iguanodon*

*Material
of cast*

Imprint of toe

STEGOSAURUS
Length: 9.1 m (30 ft)

COMPSOGNATHUS
Length: 70 cm (28 in)

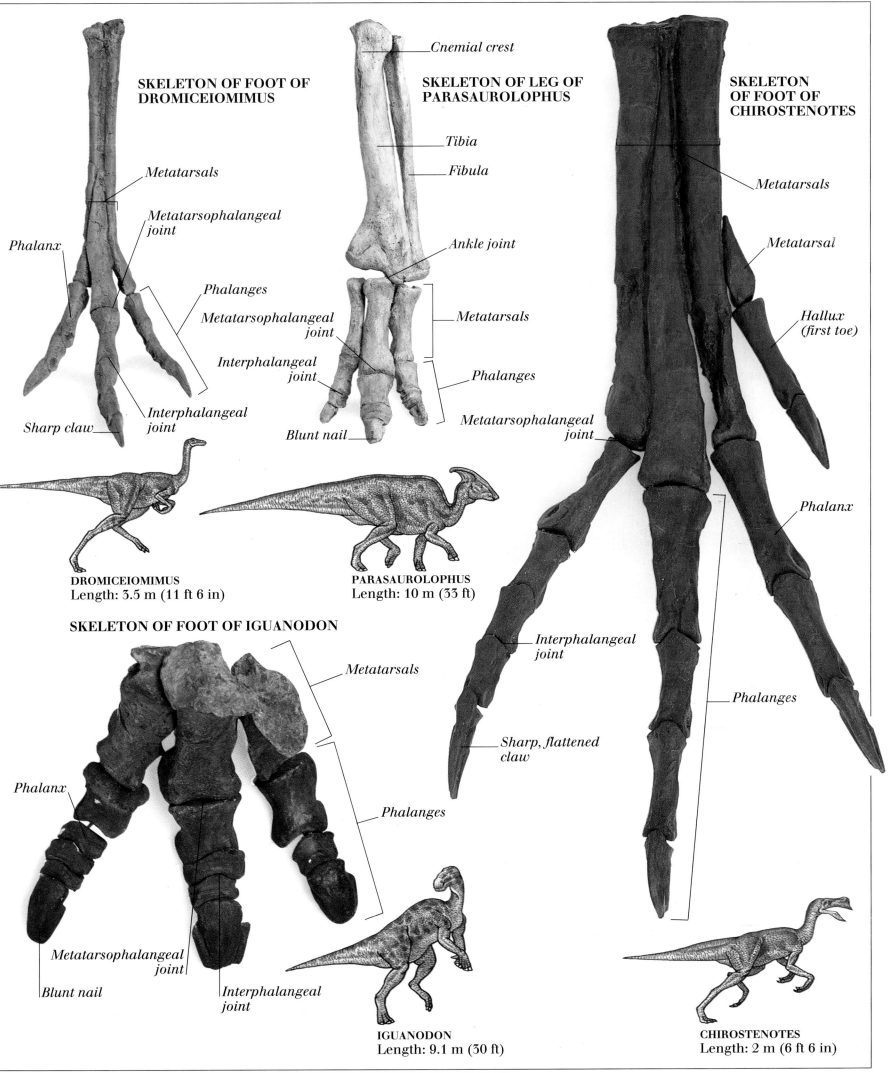

SKELETON OF FOOT OF DROMICEIOMIMUS

Metatarsals

Metatarsophalangeal joint

Phalanx

Phalanges

Metatarsophalangeal joint

Interphalangeal joint

Sharp claw

Interphalangeal joint

DROMICEIOMIMUS
Length: 3.5 m (11 ft 6 in)

SKELETON OF LEG OF PARASAUROLOPHUS

Cnemial crest

Tibia

Fibula

Ankle joint

Metatarsals

Metatarsophalangeal joint

Interphalangeal joint

Phalanges

Metatarsophalangeal joint

Blunt nail

PARASAUROLOPHUS
Length: 10 m (33 ft)

SKELETON OF FOOT OF CHIROSTENOTES

Metatarsals

Metatarsal

Hallux (first toe)

Phalanx

Interphalangeal joint

Sharp, flattened claw

Phalanges

CHIROSTENOTES
Length: 2 m (6 ft 6 in)

SKELETON OF FOOT OF IGUANODON

Metatarsals

Phalanx

Phalanges

Metatarsophalangeal joint

Blunt nail

Interphalangeal joint

IGUANODON
Length: 9.1 m (30 ft)

Dinosaur relatives

DINOSAURS BECAME EXTINCT about 65 million years ago but animals related to them still exist today. The only two surviving groups of dinosaur relatives are birds and crocodiles. Birds are generally considered to be the closest living relatives of dinosaurs, although the exact relationship between the two is controversial. One theory suggests that birds and dinosaurs diverged from a common ancestor during the Early Jurassic (208–188 million years ago). However, the most widely accepted view is that birds evolved from small, bipedal (two-legged) dinosaurs such as *Coelophysis*. The principal evidence for this relationship is the similarity between the limb bones of *Coelophysis*, *Archaeopteryx* (the oldest known bird), and modern birds: all have forelimbs with three digits, and hind limbs with four toes, one of which is a reversed hallux (first toe). Possibly descended from *Archaeopteryx* were *Ichthyornis* and *Hesperornis*, both birds of the Late Cretaceous (97.5–65 million years ago), and the more modern (but extinct) *Diatryma*, *Palaeospheniscus*, and *Presbyornis*, as well as present-day birds. Crocodiles are only remotely related to the dinosaurs, because the two groups evolved along different lines after splitting off from a common ancestral group during the Early Triassic (248–243 million years ago).

**FOSSIL OF A
BIRD'S FEATHER**

HESPERORNIS REGALIS
Length: 1.8 m (6 ft)

**EVOLUTION OF A
BIRD'S WING**

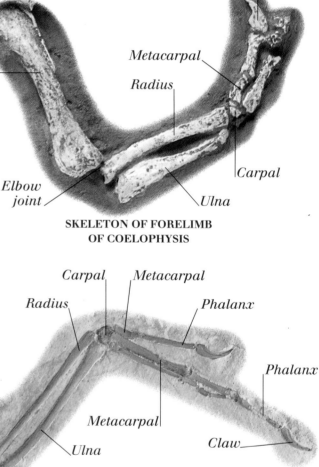

Claw

Metacarpal

Radius

Humerus

Elbow
joint

Carpal

Ulna

**SKELETON OF FORELIMB
OF COELOPHYSIS**

EXTERNAL FEATURES OF ARCHAEOPTERYX

Claw

Finger

Eye

Beak

Feather

Neck

Feather

Bony tail
core

Hind limb

Knee

Tail
feather

Ankle

Reversed hallux
(first toe)

Toe

Claw

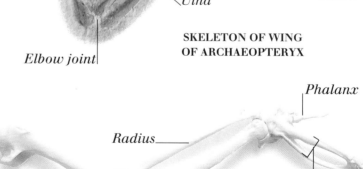

Carpal   Metacarpal

Radius

Phalanx

Humerus

Phalanx

Metacarpal

Ulna

Claw

**SKELETON OF WING
OF ARCHAEOPTERYX**

Phalanx

Radius

Carpometacarpus

Humerus

Phalanx

Ulna

Elbow joint

Phalanx

**SKELETON OF WING
OF MODERN BIRD**

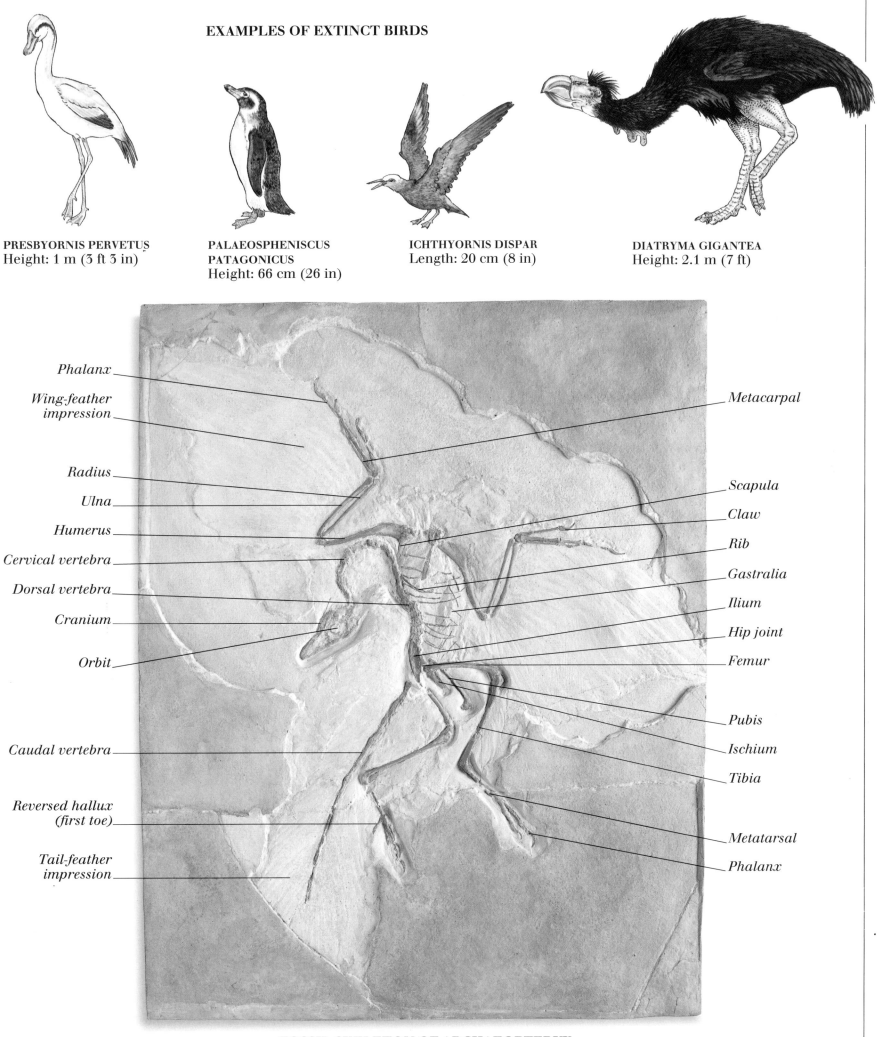

EXAMPLES OF EXTINCT BIRDS

PRESBYORNIS PERVETUS
Height: 1 m (3 ft 3 in)

PALAEOSPHENISCUS PATAGONICUS
Height: 66 cm (26 in)

ICHTHYORNIS DISPAR
Length: 20 cm (8 in)

DIATRYMA GIGANTEA
Height: 2.1 m (7 ft)

Phalanx

Wing-feather impression

Radius

Ulna

Humerus

Cervical vertebra

Dorsal vertebra

Cranium

Orbit

Caudal vertebra

Reversed hallux (first toe)

Tail-feather impression

Metacarpal

Scapula

Claw

Rib

Gastralia

Ilium

Hip joint

Femur

Pubis

Ischium

Tibia

Metatarsal

Phalanx

FOSSIL SKELETON OF ARCHAEOPTERYX

Dinosaur classification

THE CLASSIFICATION OF DINOSAURS is controversial and is continually being revised in the light of new fossil finds and reinterpretations of existing evidence. Furthermore, there are a number of different methods of classification. The method used here is based on inherited features shared by members of a group but not by any members in other groups. According to this classification, all dinosaurs and their relatives belong to the major group Archosauria (ruling reptiles). The Archosauria can be split into two main divisions: primitive archosaurs, which include Proterosuchia, Erythrosuchia, *Euparkeria*, and Crurotarsi; and ornithodiran archosaurs, which include Pterosauria, *Lagosuchus*, and the Dinosauria. The Dinosauria ("true" dinosaurs) can be divided in turn into three groups: Herrerasauria (early predatory dinosaurs), Saurischia (lizard-hipped dinosaurs), and Ornithischia (bird-hipped dinosaurs). Each group can then be subdivided down to the levels of families (with names ending in "-idae"), genera (indicated by italics in this chart) and species.

KEY

- ARCHOSAURS (RULING REPTILES)
- PRIMITIVE ARCHOSAURS
- ORNITHODIRAN ARCHOSAURS
- FLYING ARCHOSAURS
- DINOSAUR-LIKE ARCHOSAURS
- DINOSAURS
- EARLY PREDATORY DINOSAURS
- LIZARD-HIPPED DINOSAURS
- BIRD-HIPPED DINOSAURS

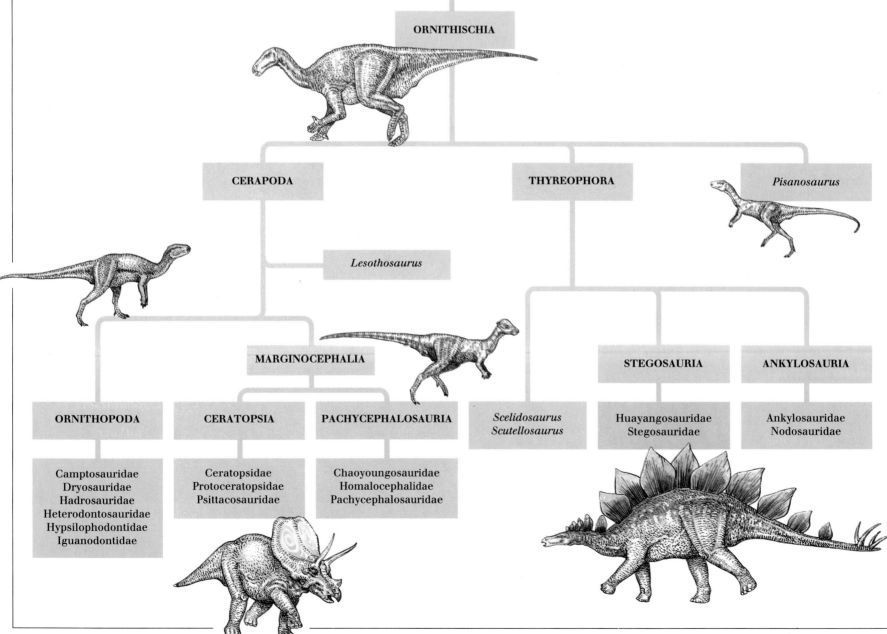

ORNITHISCHIA

CERAPODA

THYREOPHORA

Pisanosaurus

Lesothosaurus

MARGINOCEPHALIA

STEGOSAURIA

ANKYLOSAURIA

ORNITHOPODA

CERATOPSIA

PACHYCEPHALOSAURIA

Scelidosaurus
Scutellosaurus

Huayangosauridae
Stegosauridae

Ankylosauridae
Nodosauridae

Camptosauridae
Dryosauridae
Hadrosauridae
Heterodontosauridae
Hypsilophodontidae
Iguanodontidae

Ceratopsidae
Protoceratopsidae
Psittacosauridae

Chaoyoungosauridae
Homalocephalidae
Pachycephalosauridae

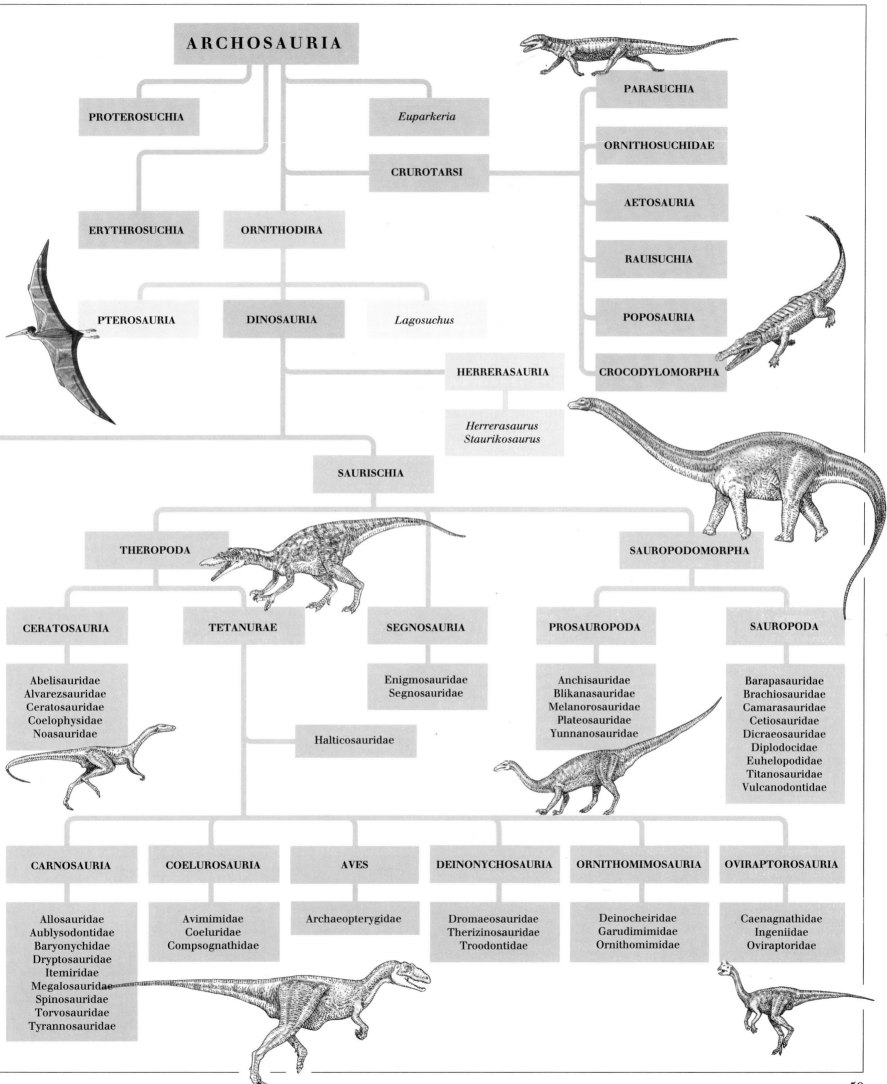

ARCHOSAURIA

PROTEROSUCHIA

Euparkeria

PARASUCHIA

ORNITHOSUCHIDAE

CRUROTARSI

AETOSAURIA

ERYTHROSUCHIA

ORNITHODIRA

RAUISUCHIA

POPOSAURIA

PTEROSAURIA

DINOSAURIA

Lagosuchus

CROCODYLOMORPHA

HERRERASAURIA

Herrerasaurus
Staurikosaurus

SAURISCHIA

THEROPODA

SAUROPODOMORPHA

CERATOSAURIA

TETANURAE

SEGNOSAURIA

PROSAUROPODA

SAUROPODA

Abelisauridae
Alvarezsauridae
Ceratosauridae
Coelophysidae
Noasauridae

Enigmosauridae
Segnosauridae

Anchisauridae
Blikanasauridae
Melanorosauridae
Plateosauridae
Yunnanosauridae

Barapasauridae
Brachiosauridae
Camarasauridae
Cetiosauridae
Dicraeosauridae
Diplodocidae
Euhelopodidae
Titanosauridae
Vulcanodontidae

Halticosauridae

CARNOSAURIA

COELUROSAURIA

AVES

DEINONYCHOSAURIA

ORNITHOMIMOSAURIA

OVIRAPTOROSAURIA

Allosauridae
Aublysodontidae
Baryonychidae
Dryptosauridae
Itemiridae
Megalosauridae
Spinosauridae
Torvosauridae
Tyrannosauridae

Avimimidae
Coeluridae
Compsognathidae

Archaeopterygidae

Dromaeosauridae
Therizinosauridae
Troodontidae

Deinocheiridae
Garudimimidae
Ornithomimidae

Caenagnathidae
Ingeniidae
Oviraptoridae

Index

61

Acknowledgments

Dorling Kindersley would like to thank:
Dr Monty Reid, Andrew Neuman, and the staff at the Royal Tyrrell Museum of Palaeontology, Drumheller, Alberta; Dr Angela Milner and the staff at the Department of Palaeontology, the Natural History Museum, London; Professor W. Ziegler and the staff, in particular Michael Loderstaedt, at the Naturmuseum Senckenburg, Frankfurt; Dr Alexander Liebau, Axel Hunghrebüller, Reiner Schoch, and the staff at the Institut und Museum für Geologie und Paläontologie der Universität, Tübingen; Rupert Wild at the Institut für Paläontologie, Staatliches Museum für Naturkunde, Stuttgart; Dr Scheiber, the Stadtmuseum, Nördlingen; Professor Dr Dietrich Herm, Staatssammlung für Paläontologie und Historische Geologie, München; Dr Michael Keith-Lucas, Department of Botany, University of Reading; Dr Richard Walker. For skeletons: the Royal Tyrrell Museum of Palaeontology, Alberta: *Dromaeosaurus* pp. 16-17, *Gryposaurus* pp. 38-39, *Heterodontosaurus* p. 35, *Maiasaura* p. 38, *Ornitholestes* p. 15, *Ornithomimus* pp. 18-19, *Parasaurolophus* pp. 40-41, *Stegoceras* pp. 46-47,

Struthiomimus p. 19, *Triceratops* pp. 50-51; Naturmuseum Senckenberg, Frankfurt: *Archaeopteryx* p. 57, *Diplodocus* pp. 28-29, *Iguanodon* p. 36, *Tyrannosaurus* pp. 22-23, *Stegosaurus* p. 43; Institut und Museum für Geologic und Paläontologie der Universität Tübingen: *Plateosaurus* pp. 24-25, *Kentrosaurus* p. 43; the Natural History Museum, London: *Baryonyx* p. 21, *Tuojiangosaurus* p. 43; Staatliches Museum für Naturkunde, Stuttgart: *Coelophysis* p. 15, *Compsognathus* p. 14; American Museum of Natural History, New York: *Protoceratops* pp. 48-49

Model makers:
John Holmes: *Euoplocephalus* pp. 44-45, *Gallimimus* pp. 18-19, *Hypsilophodon* pp. 34-35; Roby Braun: *Anchisaurus* pp. 24-25, *Compsognathus* pp. 14-15, *Stegosaurus* pp. 42-43; Centaur Studios: *Barosaurus* pp. 28-29, *Baryonyx* pp. 20-21, *Brachiosaurus* pp. 26-27, *Corythosaurus* pp. 40-41, *Iguanodon* pp. 36-37, *Triceratops* p. 50; David Donkin: Cretaceous globe p. 13, Jurassic globe p. 11, Triassic globe p. 9

Additional consultancy:
William Lindsay

Additional photography:
John Downs, Tim Parmenter, and Colin Keates (Natural History Museum, London); Lynton Gardiner (American Museum of Natural History, New York); Steve Gorton; Dave King

Photographic assistance:
Kevin Zak; Gary Ombler

Additional design assistance:
Lesley Betts; Christina Betts

Additional editorial assistance:
Jacqui Hand; Jeanette Cossar

Index:
Kay Wright